WeightWatchers
PointsPlus®

FRUITS & VEGGIES
A to Z

WeightWatchers®
PointsPlus®

FRUITS &
VEGGIES
A *to* Z

Get produce passionate with our
175 Delicious Recipes

Every Recipe Serves One

About WeightWatchers.

Weight Watchers International, Inc., is the world's leading provider of weight-management services, operating globally through a network of company-owned and franchise operations. Weight Watchers holds nearly 50,000 weekly meetings worldwide, at which members receive group support and education about healthful eating patterns, behavior modification, and physical activity. Weight-loss and weight-management results vary by individual. We recommend that you attend Weight Watchers meetings to benefit from the supportive environment you find there and follow the comprehensive Weight Watchers program, which includes a food plan, an activity plan, and a behavioral component. In addition, Weight Watchers offers a wide range of products, publications, and programs for people interested in weight loss and weight control. For the Weight Watchers meeting nearest you, call **1-800-651-6000.** For information about bringing Weight Watchers to your workplace, call **1-800-8AT-WORK.** Also visit us at our Web site, **weightwatchers.com,** and look for **Weight Watchers Magazine** at your newsstand or in your meeting room.

Contents

WEIGHT WATCHERS PUBLISHING GROUP

Editorial Director Nancy Gagliardi

Creative Director Ed Melnitsky

Photo Director Deborah Hardt

Managing Editor Sarah Wharton

Editorial Assistant Katerina Gkionis

Food Editor Eileen Runyan

Writer Alice Thompson

Recipe Developer Maureen Luchejko

Production Manager Alan Biederman

Photographers Antonis Achilleos (recipes, still life images)

David Malosh (chart images)

Food Stylist Adrienne Anderson

Prop Stylist Paige Hicks

Art Director Priest + Grace

Designer Gary Tooth, Empire Design Studio

About Our Recipes

While losing weight isn't only about what you eat, Weight Watchers realizes the critical role it plays in your success and overall good health. That's why our philosophy is to offer great-tasting, easy recipes that are nutritious as well as delicious. We make every attempt to use wholesome ingredients and to ensure that our recipes fall within the recommendations of the U.S. Dietary Guidelines for Americans for a diet that promotes health and reduces the risk for disease. In accordance with the Guidelines, Weight Watchers encourages selecting lean meats, consuming plenty of fruits and vegetables and whole grains, choosing fat-free and low-fat dairy products, and limiting sodium, saturated fat, cholesterol, trans fats, added sugars, refined grains, and alcohol. If you have special dietary needs, consult with your health-care professional for advice on a diet that is best for you, then adapt these recipes to meet your specific nutritional needs.

Read This Before You Start Cooking

Recipes in this book have been developed for Weight Watchers members who are following the *PointsPlus* program. *PointsPlus* values have been calculated using Recipe Builder at **weightwatchers.com.** Please note that some of the recipes have *PointsPlus* values even when they are made from foods that have no *PointsPlus* values. Fruit and most veggies have no *PointsPlus* values when served as a snack or part of a meal, like a cup of berries with a sandwich. But if these foods are part of a recipe, their fiber and nutrient content are incorporated into the recipe calculations using our online Recipe Builder. These nutrients can affect the *PointsPlus* values.

To achieve good-health goals and get the maximum satisfaction from the foods you eat, we suggest you keep the following information in mind while preparing our recipes:

* Substitutions made to the ingredients will alter the per-serving nutritional information and may affect the *PointsPlus* value.

* Our recipes meet Weight Watchers Good Health Guidelines for eating lean proteins and fiber-rich whole grains, and having at least five servings of vegetables and fruits and two servings of low-fat or fat-free dairy products a day, while limiting your intake of saturated fat, sugar, and sodium.

* Health agencies recommend limiting sodium intake. To stay in line with this recommendation we keep sodium levels in our recipes reasonably low; to boost flavor, we often include fresh herbs or a squeeze of citrus instead of salt. If you don't have to restrict your sodium, feel free to add a touch more salt as desired.

* All recipes in this book are for one serving.

For information about the science behind lasting weight loss and more, please visit **weightwatchers.com/science.**

Shopping for Ingredients

As you learn to eat healthier and add more Weight Watchers® Power Foods to your meals, remember these tips for choosing foods wisely:

LEAN MEATS AND POULTRY Purchase lean meats and poultry, and trim them of all visible fat before cooking. When poultry is cooked with the skin on, we recommend removing the skin before eating. Nutritional information for recipes that include meat, poultry, and fish is based on cooked, skinless boneless portions (unless otherwise stated), with all visible fat trimmed.

SEAFOOD Whenever possible, our recipes call for seafood that is sustainable and deemed the most healthful for human consumption so that your choices are not only good for the oceans but also good for you. For more information about the best seafood choices and to download a pocket guide, go to **environmentaldefensefund.org** or **montereybayaquarium.org.** For information about mercury and seafood go to **weightwatchers.com.**

PRODUCE For best flavor, maximum nutrient content, and the lowest prices, buy fresh, local produce, such as vegetables, leafy greens, and fruits in season. Rinse them thoroughly before using and keep a supply of cut-up vegetables and fruits in your refrigerator for convenient, healthy snacks.

WHOLE GRAINS Explore your market for whole-grain products, such as whole wheat and whole-grain breads and pastas, brown rice, bulgur, barley, cornmeal, whole wheat couscous, oats, and quinoa to enjoy with your meals.

Preparation and Measuring

READ THE RECIPE Take a couple of minutes to read through the ingredients and directions before you start to prepare a recipe. This will prevent you from discovering midway through that you don't have an important ingredient or that a recipe requires several hours of marinating. And it's also a good idea to assemble all ingredients and utensils within easy reach before you begin a recipe.

WEIGHING AND MEASURING The success of any recipe depends on accurate weighing and measuring. The effectiveness of the Weight Watchers program and the accuracy of the nutritional analysis depend on correct measuring as well. Use the following techniques:

* Weigh food such as meat, poultry, and fish on a food scale.

* To measure liquids, use a standard glass or plastic measuring cup placed on a level surface. For amounts less than ¼ cup, use standard measuring spoons.

* To measure dry ingredients, use metal or plastic measuring cups that come in ¼-, ⅓-, ½-, and 1-cup sizes. Fill the appropriate cup and level it with the flat edge of a knife or spatula. For amounts less than ¼ cup, use standard measuring spoons.

APP
ARTIC
ARU
ASPAR
AVO

Apples

IN SEASON **September to December**

WHILE THERE ARE THOUSANDS OF APPLE VARIETIES grown worldwide, you're probably familiar with only a handful. The varieties available at supermarkets tend to be those that travel and store well rather than those that taste exceptional. Visit orchards and farmers' markets during apple season and you'll discover many lesser-known, heirloom, and local varieties, some of which are a revelation in deliciousness and character.

CHOOSING & STORING

* Look for apples that have glossy, firm, un-blemished skins. Apples should have a fresh, lightly floral fragrance; pass on any that smell musty or sour.

* Consider buying organic; conventionally grown apples have one of the highest levels of pesticide residue of any fruit.

* Keep apples in a cool area of your kitchen if you plan to use them within a few days. For longer storage, place them in a sealed plastic bag and refrigerate them up to several weeks.

* As they ripen, apples give off ethylene, a gas that may shorten the storage life of some fruits and vegetables, so store them away from other produce.

* Stop cut apples from browning by brushing them with lemon or orange juice, or keep them in a bowl of acidulated water—water to which you've added the juice of half a lemon.

TASTE TIPS

* Grate apples and add them to muffins, meatloaf, soups, salads, sandwiches, slaws, and more; they can bring moisture, natural sweetness, and extra fiber and nutrition to hundreds of dishes.

* Slice apples and add them to sand-wiches; they have a natural affinity for cheese, ham, and peanut butter.

* Pair apples with sage, rosemary, thyme, caraway, or coriander in savory dishes; pair them with cinnamon, cloves, ginger, nutmeg, star anise, or vanilla in both sweet and savory dishes.

* Mix apples with other fruits in sauces, salads, and desserts; they're excellent with berries, cranberries, figs, grapes, oranges, pears, pomegranates, and tangerines.

Apples

Braeburn

Crisp, firm, lightly tart and refreshing

BEST FOR
Eating, applesauce, pie

GOOD TO KNOW
Stores well, making it a good choice outside of apple season

Cortland

Crisp, juicy, tangy, fragrant

BEST FOR
Eating, stewing, applesauce, pie

GOOD TO KNOW
Resists browning better than most varieties

Crispin

Crisp, explosively juicy, sweet

BEST FOR
Eating, applesauce, baking

GOOD TO KNOW
Sometimes known as Matsu

Empire

Crisp, juicy, sweet-tart

BEST FOR
Eating, salads

GOOD TO KNOW
Resists browning better than most varieties

Fuji

Very crunchy, juicy, very sweet

BEST FOR
Eating, baking whole

GOOD TO KNOW
Stores well, making it a good choice outside of apple season

Gala

Crisp, juicy, sweet, fragrant, lightly spicy

BEST FOR
Eating, salads, cooking, applesauce

GOOD TO KNOW
Complex flavor makes this tops for eating raw

Golden Delicious

Juicy, very sweet, lightly honey-flavored

BEST FOR
Eating, cooking, applesauce, pie, baking

GOOD TO KNOW
Choose carefully; can become mealy and bland with age

Granny Smith

Very firm and crisp, tart to very tart

BEST FOR
Eating, slicing for sandwiches and salads, baking, applesauce, pie,

GOOD TO KNOW
A top all-purpose apple; stores well, making it a good choice outside of apple season. Resists browning better than most varieties

Gravenstein

Crisp, juicy, lightly tart

BEST FOR
Pie, sauce, baking

GOOD TO KNOW
An early-season apple,
outstanding for pie.
Stores poorly, so not
recommended after
September

Honeycrisp

Very crisp, juicy, sweet

BEST FOR
Eating, salads,
cooking, baking

GOOD TO KNOW
Outstanding for
eating raw

Jonagold

Crisp, sweet-tart

BEST FOR
Eating, applesauce, baking

GOOD TO KNOW
A cross between Jonathan
and Golden Delicious

Jonathan

Juicy, sweet-tart, spicy

BEST FOR
Eating, salads,
applesauce, pie

GOOD TO KNOW
Quality is variable, so it's
worth sampling one before
buying a lot

Lady

Very small, crisp,
sweet-tart

BEST FOR
Garnishing, eating, baking

GOOD TO KNOW
Attractive minis; classic
for garnishing platters
and surrounding
holiday roasts

McIntosh

Tender, juicy, sweet-tart

BEST FOR
Eating, salads, applesauce

GOOD TO KNOW
Cooks down very quickly;
good for sauce but not
for baking

Red Delicious

Juicy, sweet

BEST FOR
Eating, salads

GOOD TO KNOW
Stores well, but can
become mealy

Rome

Crisp, firm, sweet-tart

BEST FOR
Baking, applesauce

GOOD TO KNOW
Outstanding for
baking whole

Apples

Easy Apple Slaw

Grate 1 medium unpeeled Red Delicious apple and toss with 1 cup grated carrot, 1 tablespoon diced red onion, 2 teaspoons apple cider vinegar, and pinch each salt and pepper.

No-Cook Applesauce

Core (but don't peel) 1 medium Fuji or Honeycrisp apple and cut it into chunks. Place in food processor with ¼ cup apple juice, 1 teaspoon lemon juice, and pinch each cinnamon and nutmeg. Pulse until smooth.

Apple and Celery Root Mash

Peel, core, and chop 1 medium Golden Delicious apple. Combine with 1 cup peeled and chopped celery root and 2 tablespoons water in small saucepan. Cover and simmer until apple and celery root are very tender, about 15 minutes. Mash and stir in 1 teaspoon butter and pinch salt.

Baked Apple with Cranberries and Maple Syrup

Core (but don't peel) 1 medium Rome or Granny Smith apple. Stuff with 2 tablespoons dried cranberries, drizzle with 1 teaspoon maple syrup, and sprinkle with cinnamon. Stand in small microwavable dish and microwave on High until tender, 1–2 minutes.

Apple Slices with Peanut Butter

Cut 1 medium unpeeled McIntosh or Gala apple into 8 wedges. Spread apple slices evenly with 1 tablespoon peanut butter. Dot peanut butter evenly with 1 tablespoon raisins.

GOOD FOR YOU

Apples are an excellent source of fiber and contain high amounts of the antioxidant quercetin. Half an apple's nutrients are found in its skin, so eat them unpeeled for maximum benefit. Pesticides are also concentrated in the skin, so scrub nonorganic apples under running water for 10 seconds before eating.

Baked Apple with Cranberries
and Maple Syrup

Artichokes

IN SEASON **March to May, and October**

MOST ARTICHOKES YOU SEE IN MARKETS ARE THE LARGE, green to greenish-purple **globe** artichokes. You may also see smaller artichokes known as **baby** artichokes, although they are not actually babies since an artichoke's size is determined by its location on the plant's stalk. For example, those at the top of the stalk will be the largest, while those towards the base may grow no larger than walnuts. Although almost the entire artichoke is edible, the center, or heart, at its base is the tender reward for anyone who invests the time in cleaning and cooking these delicious beauties.

CHOOSING & STORING

* Look for firm artichokes with tightly furled leaves and plump (not dried out) stems.

* If squeezed, a fresh artichoke should offer good resistance, and the leaves should "squeak" slightly as they rub against each other.

* Brown spots or a rusty tinge on the outer leaves of an artichoke means that it has been exposed to cold, something that shouldn't affect its flavor or texture. In fact, some connoisseurs claim that these "frosted" or "winter-kissed" artichokes are particularly tasty and tender (you be the judge!).

* Store artichokes in the coolest part of the refrigerator wrapped loosely in a paper or plastic bag.

* Trim the stem end of artichokes and wrap the base of the stem in moistened paper towels if you plan to store them for more than a day or two.

HOW TO CLEAN AN ARTICHOKE

Cleaning a fresh artichoke for cooking is not a daunting task. No special skill is required, just a little time, a small sharp knife, and a bowl of cold water to which you've added the juice of half a lemon. Once cleaned, you'll drop the artichokes into this acidulated water to prevent the cut edges from turning brown while you prep the others.

* **To prepare an artichoke for cooking whole** Peel off the dark, tough petals around the base of the artichoke until you get to the petals that are lighter in color. Cut off the very top of the artichoke, cutting just below the prickly tips of the petals. Use a pair of kitchen scissors to snip off any prickly tips lower on the artichoke. Peel the tough skin off the stem with your paring knife and trim the bottom. If you need the artichokes to sit level, you may cut off the stem entirely, but don't discard it—cook it along with the artichokes. *Continued* »

Artichokes

* **To prepare an artichoke heart** Run a paring knife around the base of the artichoke, removing all petals until you get to tender ones with yellow-green bottoms. Slice off all but an inch of the top of the artichoke. Very carefully use a teaspoon or melon baller to scoop out the small petals and hairy choke at the center of the artichoke, exposing the heart. Peel the stem and leave it on or separate it from the base of the heart.

* **To prepare baby artichokes** The choke and inner leaves of baby artichokes are very tender, so all you'll need to do is trim the stem end and pull off and discard any tough outer leaves.

GOOD FOR YOU

Artichokes have been prized since ancient times for a host of medicinal powers, and modern science gives us reasons to love them too. Artichokes are a good source of potassium, folate, and fiber and contain a number of antioxidants. Preliminary studies suggest that the vegetable's unique combination of nutrients may help control blood sugar levels and lower cholesterol.

Raw Artichoke Heart Salad

PointsPlus value 2

Prepare an artichoke heart (see instructions at left); slice as thinly as possible with very sharp knife. Immediately toss with 1 teaspoon lemon juice. Toss again with 1 cup arugula, 1 teaspoon balsamic vinegar, and pinch each salt and pepper. Top with 1 tablespoon grated Parmesan.

Steamed Whole Artichoke with Garlic Vinaigrette

PointsPlus value 2

Combine 2 tablespoons red-wine vinegar, 1 minced garlic clove, 1 teaspoon olive oil, and pinch each salt and pepper in small bowl. Prepare 1 medium artichoke for cooking whole (see page 20); place on rack over simmering water, cover, and steam until a leaf from the base pulls away easily, 25–35 minutes. Serve warm with vinaigrette.

Broiled Baby Artichokes

PointsPlus value 4

Preheat broiler. Prepare 4 (1½–ounce) baby artichokes (see instructions at left); boil in lightly salted water until bases are tender when pierced with knife, 6–7 minutes. Drain; cool under cold running water. Cut artichokes lengthwise in half and place on small baking pan. Sprinkle with 1 tablespoon whole wheat bread crumbs and 2 teaspoons grated Parmesan. Drizzle with 1 teaspoon olive oil. Broil until topping is browned, 2–3 minutes. Do not turn. Serve warm or at room temperature with lemon.

Broiled Baby Artichokes

Arugula

IT MAY LOOK LIKE A LETTUCE, BUT ARUGULA IS actually a member of the cruciferous vegetable family, a nutritionally powerful group that includes broccoli, cabbage, and kale. Its peppery flavor makes a bold flavor statement in salad mixes or on its own. It's less commonly (but just as deliciously!) wilted into pastas, soups, and other hot dishes or steamed or sautéed like spinach.

CHOOSING & STORING

* Look for crisp, dark green leaves without yellowing (a sign of age) or slimy spots (a sign of poor handling).

* In general, small "baby" leaves will be tender and mild in flavor, while larger leaves will be crisper and have a pronounced peppery bite. Choose according to your preference.

* Handle arugula gently from market to kitchen to refrigerator in order to avoid bruising its fragile leaves. Arugula packaged in plastic "clamshells" has the benefit of being protected from crushing.

* Larger leaves are often sold in a bunch held together with a twist tie or rubber band. Remove whatever is holding the leaves together, then separate the leaves and discard any that look yellowed or wilted. Wrap the root ends in a damp paper towel and then wrap the whole bunch in a plastic bag.

* Use arugula within a day or two to enjoy its distinctively fresh, pungent flavor at its best.

CLEAN IT RIGHT

Arugula is grown in sandy soil, so it's important to rinse it very well before using, even if it comes in a package labeled "prewashed."

* Trim off and discard tough stems from very large leaves.

* Fill a sink or large bowl with cold water and submerge leaves completely. Swish the leaves around gently with your hands and then let the leaves soak for a few minutes; this will allow sand and grit to sink to the bottom.

* Scoop leaves up and drain in a colander or salad spinner.

* Remove any excess moisture by patting leaves between layers of paper towel or wrap in a clean kitchen towel.

GOOD FOR YOU

A cup of arugula has just 5 calories and contains vitamins A, C, and K and folate.

**Pasta Salad with Arugula
and Cherry Tomatoes**

Wilted Arugula
with Balsamic

Cook 2 thinly sliced garlic
cloves and pinch red pepper
flakes in 1 teaspoon olive oil
in skillet until fragrant, 1–2
minutes. Add 2 cups arugula,
1–2 tablespoons balsamic
vinegar, and pinch each salt
and pepper. Cook, covered,
until arugula is wilted and
just tender, 2–3 minutes.

Arugula and
Orange Salad

Place 2 cups baby arugula in
medium bowl. Peel and dice
1 orange and discard seeds;
add to arugula with 1 sliced
celery stalk, a few slices red
onion, chopped fresh dill
(optional), and 2 tablespoons
fat-free dressing.

Pasta Salad with
Arugula and
Cherry Tomatoes

Toss 2 cups arugula leaves
with ½ cup warm cooked
whole wheat bow ties or other
small pasta, ½ cup halved
cherry tomatoes, 1 tablespoon
crumbled goat cheese, and
⅛ teaspoon pepper.

Asparagus

GREEN, WHITE, AND PURPLE—WHATEVER VARIETY you prefer, the color of asparagus is more about pleasing your plate than your palate. Fact is, all varieties and sizes—pencil (very thin), medium, or jumbo—pretty much taste the same. Focus on finding the freshest stalks and you won't be disappointed.

CHOOSING & STORING

* Look for bunches of asparagus with straight, firm stalks. The tips should be tightly closed and free of slime. The cut ends of the stalks should appear fresh, not woody or wrinkled.

* Give asparagus the sniff test: It should smell fresh and earthy, not sour.

* Pick the size to match your cooking technique. Skinny pencil stalks cook very quickly and are ideal for adding to pasta, risotto, and any dish where you don't want them to overwhelm the flavors of other ingredients. Choose more substantial medium or jumbo stalks for steaming, roasting, and grilling.

* Check the amount needed in a recipe. Most bunches of asparagus weigh between 1 and 2 pounds. If you need a specific weight for a recipe, weigh it in the market.

* Think fresh: Asparagus begins losing sweetness from the moment it's harvested. Keep it refrigerated for no more than 2 to 3 days. Wrap it loosely in plastic or paper, or place the cut ends in a jar with an inch or two of water in the bottom (like a bunch of flowers) and cover the exposed stalks loosely with plastic or paper.

WHAT CHEFS KNOW

* White asparagus is very popular in Europe, where it is prized for its sweetness and tenderness. But beware: The white variety turns bitter with age or improper handling, so buy it only if it looks absolutely fresh and cook it the same day.

* Think twice before plunking down a fortune for purple asparagus. Not only is it almost identical to green asparagus in flavor, but it turns green during cooking, losing all but a tinge of its distinctive violet hue.

* Bend the stalks near the base of pencil or medium asparagus, and the woody part of the stalk will snap off.

* Don't use this snap technique for jumbo stalks; you'll loose up to half of the vegetable you paid for. Instead, cut off just the white base of the stalk with a paring knife and then use a vegetable peeler to gently remove the first couple of inches of tough skin on the stalk.

Asparagus

Asparagus and Hummus Lettuce Wraps

Start with 12 trimmed and steamed pencil or medium asparagus stalks. Lay 3 large leaves Boston lettuce on work surface. Top leaves evenly with 2 tablespoons hummus and lay 4 asparagus stalks on each. Sprinkle with lemon juice and roll leaves up to enclose filling.

Almost-Instant Asparagus Soup

Trim and chop 12 asparagus stalks. Place in small saucepan with $1\frac{1}{2}$ cups low-sodium fat-free vegetable broth, $\frac{1}{3}$ cup chopped onion, and pinch each salt and pepper. Cover and simmer until asparagus is very tender, about 8 minutes. Let cool 5 minutes. Transfer to blender and puree.

Roasted Sesame Asparagus and Scallions

Preheat oven to 450°F. Place 12 trimmed asparagus stalks in small baking pan; sprinkle with 2 tablespoons sliced scallions. Toss with 1 teaspoon toasted sesame oil and roast until soft and browned, 12–15 minutes. Sprinkle with $\frac{1}{4}$ teaspoon toasted sesame seeds.

GOOD FOR YOU

Asparagus is one of the very best sources of vitamin K, a vitamin important for bone health, and contains impressive amounts of folate (supportive of heart health and healthy pregnancy), fiber, and essential B vitamins such as thiamine and riboflavin. In addition, of all fruits and vegetables tested, asparagus contains the highest level of glutathione, an antioxidant that helps protect cells and aids liver function.

Roasted Sesame Asparagus and Scallions

Avocados

RICH AND BUTTERY, WITH A HINT OF SWEETNESS AND almost no acid, the avocado has such a unique flavor profile for a fruit that it's usually treated like a vegetable. The most commonly available avocado in the United States is the **Hass** variety, easily recognizable by its very dark green (almost black) skin with a rough, pebbly texture. Jade-green, smoother-skinned **Fuerte** and Florida avocados are milder, with flesh that is less buttery and sometimes even watery.

CHOOSING & STORING

* Choose avocados that have unblemished skins and are heavy for their size.

* Press the fruit gently near the stem end with your finger tip: If it is rock-hard it may take up to a week to ripen; if it offers just a little give, it will ripen within about 3 days; and if your finger leaves a slight indentation it is already ripe.

* Use avocados only when they're ripe; unripe avocados are nearly tasteless.

* Store unripe avocados at room temperature and ripe ones in the refrigerator for a day or two.

* Speed the ripening of avocados by placing them in a paper bag with an apple; leave at room temperature and they should be soft in 1 to 3 days.

WHAT CHEFS KNOW

* Given a choice, opt for Hass avocados: they're reliably rich and buttery in texture and superior in flavor to other varieties.

* To halve and pit an avocado, run a knife lengthwise all the way around, cutting right to the pit in the middle. Twist the halves in opposite directions, separating them. Remove the pit either by prodding and loosening it with a spoon and then lifting it out, or give it a firm whack with the blade of a heavy knife and lift it out.

* Keep avocados from browning by brushing the cut surfaces with lemon or lime juice; although unattractive, browning will not actually affect flavor or texture.

* Prevent guacamole from browning on top by pressing plastic wrap directly onto the surface of the dip; this will keep out oxygen, the culprit in browning.

Avocados

Avocado and Shrimp Bites

Cut ¼ peeled avocado into 1-inch pieces. Thread avocado and ¼ cup small cooked and peeled shrimp onto 1 (8-inch) bamboo skewer. Sprinkle with a little lime juice and pinch each ground cumin, salt, and pepper.

Spicy Avocado Lettuce Roll

Combine 1 tablespoon fat-free mayonnaise and ½ teaspoon wasabi paste in cup. Layer ¼ cup sliced cooked chicken breast, ¼ peeled and sliced papaya, and ¼ peeled and sliced avocado on 1 large green leaf lettuce leaf. Spread evenly with mayonnaise mixture. Fold two opposite sides of lettuce leaf in and roll up to enclose filling.

Avocado and Scallop Salad

Bring 1 cup water to boil in small saucepan. Add 3 small sea scallops and cook until opaque, 1–2 minutes. Drain; let cool. Whisk together 2 tablespoons red-wine vinegar, 1 tablespoon chopped parsley, 1 tablespoon chopped cilantro, 1 teaspoon olive oil, 1 minced garlic clove, and pinch each salt and pepper in medium bowl. Add scallops and ¼ peeled and sliced avocado; toss gently to coat. Mound onto 2 Bibb or Boston lettuce leaves.

GOOD FOR YOU

A combination of monounsaturated fats, potassium, and vitamin E make avocados an excellent food choice for promoting the health of your heart. And there's more good news about these delicious fruits: They're packed with vitamin K and contain fiber and vitamin B_6.

Avocado and Scallop Salad

BAN
BEETS
BELGIAN
BELL
BLAC
BLUEBE

BRUSS
SF

ANAS

ENDIVE

PEPPERS

K BERRIES

RRIES

BROCCOLI

ELS

ROUTS

Bananas

ALTHOUGH HUNDREDS OF BANANA VARIETIES ARE grown worldwide, the slender yellow **Cavendish** variety is by far the most popular and is widely available in the United States. If you can find them, **dwarf** or **finger** bananas are a real treat: These miniatures are supersweet, with a flavor that's slightly more floral and less musky than that of regular bananas. Less common are stocky **red** bananas, which turn deep-red to purple when ripe and have sweet, creamy, pink-tinged flesh.

CHOOSING & STORING

Bananas are one of the few fruits that ripen better in your kitchen than they do on the plant, and that's good news since the majority of bananas in our markets are grown in South and Central America and shipped out green. It also means there's little guesswork involved when it comes to picking out a good bunch: Just look for smooth, unblemished skins that have few (if any) black spots. Allow the fruit to ripen at room temperature.

* Speed up the ripening process by storing bananas in a paper bag with an apple.

* Refrigeration will permanently halt the ripening process, so refrigerate your bananas only if they have already reached ideal sweetness; the skins will continue to darken although the flesh will remain unchanged.

* Faced with a glut of over-ripening bananas? Freeze them! Peel, slice, wrap well in plastic, and freeze for up to 6 months. They can even go right from the freezer into the blender for smoothies.

ALL ABOUT RIPENESS

Almost everyone has an opinion when it comes to how ripe the ideal banana should be. Some prefer the firmer, mildly flavored flesh of a fruit whose green skin is just barely tinged with yellow, while others crave the sweeter, softer, riper flesh of a yellow fruit spotted with black. Personal preference aside, there are a few rules of thumb for using bananas in recipes.

* **Cooking or roasting whole** Greener, firmer, less ripe bananas are preferable since they'll hold their shape better.

* **Slicing and eating raw or frozen** Bright-yellow, medium-ripe fruit that's sweet but still not mushy is ideal.

* **Mashing and baking** Very ripe fruit that's spotted with brown will have the softest texture and fullest flavor, making it ideal for recipes like banana bread.

Bananas

Banana Smoothie

Peel and slice 1 small banana. Wrap in plastic wrap and freeze until firm, about 30 minutes. Puree slices in blender with ½ cup fat-free milk, 2 ice cubes, and a few drops vanilla extract. Pour into glass and sprinkle with 1 teaspoon unsweetened cocoa powder.

Roasted Banana with Chocolate and Sea Salt

Preheat oven to 475°F. Cut 1 small unpeeled banana lengthwise until almost split in half. Sprinkle with 2 teaspoons chocolate chips. Close banana and place on small foil-lined baking sheet. Roast until banana is soft and chocolate is melted, about 10 minutes. Peel banana and sprinkle with a few pinches coarse sea salt.

Peanut Butter–Banana Pop

Insert 1 (6-inch) bamboo skewer lengthwise into 1 small banana, or cut the banana into chunks and thread the chunks onto the skewer. Cover with plastic wrap and freeze on wax-paper–lined plate for 30 minutes. Place 1 tablespoon creamy peanut butter in small microwavable bowl. Microwave on High, stirring once or twice, until warm and thin, about 15 seconds. Spread peanut butter evenly over banana and freeze on wax-paper–lined plate until set, about 30 minutes.

GOOD FOR YOU

A medium banana delivers a whopping amount (over 450 mg) of potassium. Couple that with a low 1 mg of sodium, and you have such an ideal sodium-to-potassium ratio that, as part of a healthy diet, the fruit may help to reduce the risk of high blood pressure and stroke.

Peanut Butter–Banana Pop

Beets

IN SEASON June to October

ONCE CONSIDERED STAID, STODGY, OR JUST DOWNRIGHT unappetizing, beets have undergone a culinary renaissance. Vibrant, earthy-tasting **red** beets are the most commonly available, but specialty stores and farmers' markets now offer a dazzling array of colors and sizes. Look for sweet, mild **golden** beets, either mature or in baby form; golden beets won't stain your hands or cutting board as aggressively as red beets, making them a good choice for using raw in salads and slaws. Also look for whimsical white-and-red-striped **candy cane,** or **Chioggia**, beets, which are almost always sold while still small.

CHOOSING & STORING

* Look for beets that are firm, not flabby, with skin that is free of cuts and discoloration.

* Small or medium beets are usually sweeter and tenderer than larger beets, so try to buy them no larger than baseballs.

* If the beet greens are attached, they should be bright-green and fresh-looking. The greens will leach moisture from your beets, so cut them off about a 1/2 inch above the top before storing.

* Place beets in a plastic bag and refrigerate up to several weeks. Greens should be wrapped in a paper towel, placed in a paper bag, and refrigerated for no more than a day or two before cooking.

WHAT CHEFS KNOW

* Trim and peel beets after cooking, not before, so that their color (and some nutrients) won't bleed out.

* Roasting concentrates beets' flavor and sweetness and is super simple. Just wrap the beets in foil and place on the rack of a 375°F oven until tender, 30 to 60 minutes depending on size. Let cool and rub skins off with a paper towel.

* Raw beets are a fabulous addition to salads and slaws. Shred them on the large holes of a box grater or with the shredding attachment of a food processor.

* Cook beet greens any way you would kale (see page 114).

* Removing red beet juice stains from cutting boards is difficult; speed cleanup by covering your board with parchment paper before chopping beets. Avoid beet stains altogether by cooking with golden rather than red beets.

Beets

Grated Beet Slaw

Toss 1 cup peeled and grated beets in small bowl with ½ cup halved grapes, 1 small grated carrot, 3 thinly sliced scallions, 2 teaspoons apple cider vinegar, and pinch each salt and pepper.

Roast Beets with Ginger

Preheat oven to 400°F. Wrap 2 (6-ounce) medium beets in aluminum foil and roast until fork-tender when pierced with tip of knife, about 45 minutes. Allow beets to cool slightly, then rub lightly with paper towels to remove skins. Slice beets and toss in bowl with 1 teaspoon each rice wine vinegar, soy sauce, and grated fresh ginger.

Beef and Beet Hash

Combine ¾ cup diced cooked beets with 2 ounces trimmed and chopped cooked beef sirloin, ½ small grated potato, ¼ cup chopped onion, and 2 tablespoons water in small skillet. Cook, covered, until potato and onion are tender, 8–10 minutes. Garnish with parsley if you like.

GOOD FOR YOU

In addition to healthy amounts of folate, potassium, and fiber, beets boast a unique blend of powerful nutrient compounds. Of particular interest to researchers are beets' betalains, a group of antioxidants that may contribute to heart health and protect against some cancers, particularly colon cancer. Don't forget the beet greens—they're a good source of iron and beta-carotene.

Beef and Beet Hash

Belgian Endive

IN SEASON **Year-round**

LOVELY, VERSATILE BELGIAN ENDIVE HAS BEEN CULTIVATED only since the 1830s, making it a relative newcomer to the vegetable market. Most Americans know it as a crunchy, pleasantly bitter addition to salads, while Europeans are more likely to cook it until it turns sweet and meltingly tender. The classic Belgian endive, sometimes known as **white Belgian endive**, is a pale beauty with glossy white leaves tipped in greenish yellow. Look also for **California,** or **red, endive,** a cross between Belgian endive and radicchio.

CHOOSING & STORING

∗ Choose densely packed, solid heads of absolutely crisp leaves.

∗ Belgian endive will turn green and bitter when exposed to light, which is why the heads are often wrapped in tissue. If yours aren't, you can wrap them in a paper towel before placing them in a loosely sealed plastic bag.

∗ Keep Belgian endive in the crisper drawer of your refrigerator and it should stay sweet and crunchy for a week or two.

∗ Only the very outer leaves on the head need to be rinsed before serving.

GOOD FOR YOU

Belgian endive is an excellent source of beta-carotene and vitamin K.

WHAT CHEFS KNOW

∗ Not a fan of endive's bitterness? The vegetable's pungency is concentrated towards the base of the leaves and in the head's core; removing these parts will lessen its bite if you're serving it raw. Cooking also neutralizes its bitterness, leaving it mild and quite sweet.

∗ Red endive loses its distinctive scarlet hue with cooking, so it's best to use it raw.

∗ Don't use cast iron to cook endive or it may turn an unappealing gray color, although its flavor won't be compromised.

∗ Just about anything you can spread on a cracker you can spoon into raw endive leaves: dips, soft cheeses, seafood salads, salsas, and more.

2 PointsPlus value

Endive with Shaved Parmesan

Separate leaves from 1 small endive and arrange on plate. Sprinkle with 1 tablespoon chopped fresh parsley leaves, 2 teaspoons lemon juice, and 2 tablespoons shaved Parmesan.

2 PointsPlus value

Braised Endive

Cut 1 small endive lengthwise in half. Place cut side down in small skillet with ¼ cup low-sodium fat-free chicken broth, 1 teaspoon apple cider vinegar, 1 teaspoon olive oil, and pinch each salt and pepper. Cover and simmer until endive is fork-tender, about 5 minutes.

3 PointsPlus value

Herbed Ricotta– Stuffed Endive

Combine ½ cup fat-free ricotta cheese with 1 teaspoon chopped fresh chives, 1 teaspoon grated lemon zest, and pinch of pepper. Separate 8 leaves from 1 small endive. Spoon 1 tablespoon ricotta mixture onto each leaf, and sprinkle with a little more chopped chives and zest.

Bell Peppers

BELL PEPPERS COME IN A RAINBOW OF COLORS, INCLUDING the common red, yellow, and green varieties, plus orange, brown, purple and more. Green bell peppers are fully mature but less ripe than their red and yellow counterparts and, as a result, less sweet. **Holland** peppers (grown in greenhouses) are known for their uniform shape and very thick, crunchy, heavy flesh. **Field** peppers (grown outdoors) tend to be more irregular in shape and have thinner flesh.

CHOOSING & STORING

* Look for peppers with smooth, shiny skin and a stem end that looks fresh and green (not brown or dried out).

* Holland peppers have a higher water content than field peppers and will be quite heavy and often startlingly expensive. The good news is that they are available year-round and are generally excellent in flavor and texture.

* Store bell peppers in a plastic bag in the refrigerator for up to a week. You can also seed and dice peppers and freeze them for up to 3 months.

* Bell peppers are one of the vegetables with the most residual pesticides, so consider buying organic if possible.

WHAT CHEFS KNOW

* A common complaint is that raw bell peppers are hard to digest. It's actually the skin, not the flesh, that is responsible for digestive issues. You can use a vegetable peeler to remove the skin if you like; smoother, larger, less creviced peppers will be easier to peel, so buy Holland peppers if you want to try this.

* Roasting intensifies peppers' sweetness and makes them an ideal base for soups and sauces. To roast peppers whole, place them on a parchment-lined baking sheet and roast at 425°F until skin is browned and blistered, 15 to 20 minutes. Transfer peppers to a paper bag, seal the bag, and cool for 10 minutes. Remove stem and seeds and rub off the skin.

* You can also grill peppers over medium-hot coals for about 10 minutes, turning them frequently with tongs. Cool and clean them in the same way as roasted peppers.

_Bell Peppers

Red Pepper Soup

Chop 2 small red bell peppers and sauté in 1 teaspoon olive oil in small nonstick saucepan until tender. Add 1 cup low-sodium fat-free chicken broth and ½ cup canned diced tomatoes. Puree in food processor. Sprinkle with 2 tablespoons chopped fresh basil.

Greek Grilled Vegetables

Cut 1 bell pepper into quarters. Halve 1 baby (4-ounce) eggplant and 1 small yellow squash. Place on plate with 3 whole scallions; lightly spray vegetables with nonstick spray and sprinkle with ⅛ teaspoon salt. Grill vegetables over medium-high heat, turning, until browned and tender, about 8 minutes. Serve sprinkled with juice of ½ lemon, 2 tablespoons pitted sliced kalamata olives, and 1 tablespoon oregano leaves.

Pepper Strips and Dip

Combine 1 cup plain fat-free Greek yogurt in small bowl with 1 teaspoon chopped chipotles en adobo and 1 tablespoon chopped fresh cilantro. Cut 1 medium red bell pepper into strips and serve with dip.

Bell Pepper "Nachos"

Cut 1 bell pepper lengthwise in half. Place in small microwavable dish. Spoon ¼ cup drained and rinsed black beans into each pepper half. Top each half with 2 tablespoons _pico de gallo_ and 1 (½-ounce) slice reduced-fat pepper Jack cheese. Cover and microwave on High until filling is hot and cheese is melted, about 1 minute.

GOOD FOR YOU

All bell peppers are packed with vitamins and minerals, and certain colors have even more of the good stuff than others. A yellow bell pepper has five times as much vitamin C as an orange bell pepper. Yellow, orange, and red peppers contain more of the antioxidant beta-carotene than the green variety; and red peppers are one of the few vegetables that contain the powerful antioxidant lycopene.

Bell Pepper "Nachos"

Blackberrie

IN SEASON June to August

UNTIL FAIRLY RECENTLY THESE DELICIOUS BERRIES had the reputation of being too sour for snacking and too thorny for cultivation. But thanks to the discovery of their antioxidant bonanza, plus the development of thornless bushes, blackberries are now more readily available and more popular than ever.

CHOOSING & STORING

* Look for plump berries, and beware those that have small bits of stem attached: They may have been picked too early and may not ripen properly.

* Softness rather than color is the best indication of blackberry ripeness.

* Refrigerate berries for as short a time as possible. They lose flavor rapidly once harvested and can go from ripe and wonderful to mushy and moldy in a day or two.

* Freeze blackberries if you're lucky enough to have a surplus. Place them in a single layer on a parchment-lined baking sheet and pop into the freezer until solid, 1 to 2 hours. Then transfer them to a zip-close plastic freezer bag and freeze for up to 6 months.

GOOD FOR YOU

High fiber and a big dose of antioxidants make blackberries a great choice for snacking, cooking, and baking.

TASTE TIPS

* Blackberries' sweet-tart flavor make them a wonderful accompaniment to duck, pork, or game. They can be roasted or cooked down in a pan sauce or used as a raw garnish on the finished dish.

* Blackberries are excellent when mixed with sweeter fruits like pears, apples, melons, and strawberries.

* You can substitute blackberries in almost any recipe calling for raspberries. They're usually tangier than their red cousins, so adjust sugar or other flavorings accordingly.

* Turn a glass of sparkling water into a nonalcoholic cocktail by adding a few blackberries and a small sprig of mint or basil. Works for sparkling wine, too!

Chicken, Blackberry, and Spinach Salad

3 PointsPlus value

Blackberries with Apples and Arugula

Toss together 2 cups arugula, 1 cup blackberries, and 1 small thinly sliced Granny Smith apple in bowl. Sprinkle with 1 tablespoon lemon juice and ¼ teaspoon salt.

4 PointsPlus value

Blackberry Crush

Puree 1 (6-ounce) container blackberries, ½ medium ripe banana, 4 ice cubes, 1 teaspoon maple syrup, and 1 teaspoon almond extract in blender.

4 PointsPlus value

Chicken, Blackberry, and Spinach Salad

Toss 2 cups baby spinach in bowl with 1 cup blackberries, ½ cup cooked cubed chicken breast, and 1 tablespoon balsamic vinegar.

Blueberries

IN SEASON **April to September**

THESE POWERFUL LITTLE BERRIES ARE PACKED WITH SO much good stuff that some people refer to them as "brain berries" or "youth berries." And with a sweet-tart balance to rival any other berry, plus virtually no seeds, blueberries come pretty close to being the perfect fruit. Almost all the blueberries sold fresh in the United States are known as **cultivated,** or **highbush,** berries. The smaller **wild,** or **lowbush,** berries are usually sold frozen. While wild berries have the distinction of being slightly higher in antioxidants than their cultivated brethren, their flavor is less vibrant.

CHOOSING & STORING

* Look for plump, firm berries covered with the dusty, silvery bloom that's a sign of freshness.

* Buy only berries that are blue-black or deep indigo or purple; redness is a sign that the berries have been picked too early.

* Blueberries are usually sold in baskets. If you can, check that squished, moldy, or wrinkly berries haven't been hidden near the bottom.

* Refrigerate berries, loosely covered, for a few days; they will mold quickly after that.

* Blueberries are one of the easiest berries to freeze. Just place unwashed berries loosely in an airtight container and freeze for up to 6 months. Thaw and use over yogurt or in cereal, or add frozen to batter for baked goods or to smoothies.

WHAT CHEFS KNOW

* Blueberries are just as delicious in savory dishes as they are in sweet ones. Their flavor pairs particularly well with cinnamon, ginger, lemon, thyme, shallots, almonds, yogurts, and soft cheeses.

* Substitute frozen blueberries if fresh are out of season; the texture of frozen berries is a little mushy, but the flavor is excellent. If using frozen berries in pancakes or muffins, add them in their frozen state to prevent their juices from bleeding too much into the batter.

* Add a few handfuls of fresh blueberries to your next salad, or blend fresh or frozen berries with a little vinegar, shallot, salt, and pepper for an excellent fat-free dressing.

* Rub your hands with lemon juice to help remove blueberry stains.

Blueberries

Blueberries Jubilee

Heat ½ cup blueberries, 1 tablespoon orange juice, and 1 teaspoon peeled and minced ginger in small saucepan until mixture bubbles and thickens, 2–3 minutes. Cool slightly, then spoon over ½ cup fat-free vanilla frozen yogurt.

Blueberry-Oatmeal Pudding

Place ½ cup warm oatmeal (cooked with water) in bowl. Stir in 3 tablespoons light vanilla soy milk, ½ cup blueberries, 1 teaspoon currants, 1 teaspoon maple syrup, and sprinkling of cinnamon and nutmeg. Serve warm or chilled.

Berries with Cottage Cheese and Walnuts

Toss together 1 cup blueberries and 1 tablespoon chopped walnuts in bowl. Spoon over ⅔ cup fat-free cottage cheese and sprinkle with dash of cinnamon.

GOOD FOR YOU

Because of their outstanding antioxidant content, blueberries may help lower the risk of cancer, help prevent cardiovascular disease, and improve brain function. That's a lot for a little berry!

Blueberries Jubilee

Broccoli

IN SEASON October to February

DELICIOUS, VERSATILE, AND OUTRAGEOUSLY HEALTHFUL— there's a lot to love about broccoli. It was one of the first vegetables to be recognized as a health-protecting "superfood," and ongoing research continues to polish its nutritional virtues. Broccoli also has a few relatives you should look out for at the market. **Broccolini** is a hybrid variety with long, slender stems; its flavor is similar to broccoli, but you're better off cooking it as you would asparagus (see page 26). **Broccoli rabe** is another delicious family member that is excellent steamed or sautéed.

CHOOSING & STORING

* Look for broccoli with firm, dark-green to purple-green floret clusters without yellow blossoms (a sign of age).

* Give it the sniff test: Broccoli should smell fresh and earthy, not sour or cabbagey.

* Refrigerate broccoli in a paper or plastic bag in the vegetable drawer of your refrigerator. Although broccoli will keep a fresh appearance for a week or more, it rapidly becomes bitter and woody, so try to use it within a few days for best flavor.

* Visit a farmers' market in the fall for broccoli at its crispest and sweetest—a real treat!

GOOD FOR YOU

Broccoli is packed with vitamin C and contains a terrific amount of heart-healthy potassium. And there's more: This vegetable boasts beta-carotene and a number of phytochemicals, including sulforaphane and indoles, that studies suggest may reduce the risk of some cancers.

COOK IT RIGHT

* Overcooking can turn the freshest broccoli into a khaki, tasteless mush. Keep cooking times short to preserve its flavor and famously crisp texture.

* Cut florets into uniform size and cook only until they turn bright green and stems are barely flexible. That means just 4 to 5 minutes of steaming or grilling, about 3 minutes of sautéing, and about 2 minutes of boiling or microwaving.

* Don't overlook eating broccoli raw; it's a crunchy classic on crudité platters and wonderfully refreshing as the basis for a vegetable salad.

* Remember that even broccoli's thick, sometimes woody stalks are edible (and delicious). Separate the stalk from the crown, and peel off the thick, fibrous skin—you'll have a tender bit of juicy flesh. Slice it and cook it along with the florets, munch it raw, or grate it for salads or slaws.

Broccoli

Steamed Broccoli with Ginger Sauce

Steam 1 cup broccoli florets just until bright green and crisp-tender, about 4 minutes; transfer to small bowl. Toss with 1 tablespoon reduced-sodium soy sauce, 1 teaspoon grated ginger, 1 teaspoon lemon juice, and 1 tablespoon water.

Creamy Broccoli Salad

Combine 1 tablespoon fat-free mayonnaise, 1 tablespoon golden raisins, and 1 teaspoon white-wine vinegar in small bowl. Add 1 cup small broccoli florets and ½ chopped red apple.

Easy Broccoli with Feta and Shells

Steam 1 cup small broccoli florets. While still warm, toss with ½ cup cooked whole wheat shell pasta, 1 tablespoon crumbled feta, 2 tablespoons warm chicken or vegetable broth, and lots of black pepper.

Crunchy Deviled Chicken with Roasted Broccoli and Peppers

Preheat oven to 425°F. Spray small baking pan with nonstick spray. Combine 1 teaspoon light mayonnaise, 1 teaspoon Dijon mustard, and pinch each salt and cayenne pepper in cup. Sprinkle 2 tablespoons plain panko bread crumbs on sheet of wax paper. Brush mayonnaise mixture on 1 small (2 ½-ounce) skinless chicken drumstick. Roll in crumbs to coat. Place in pan; lightly spray with nonstick spray. Scatter 1 cup broccoli florets, ½ chopped bell pepper, and ½ small sliced red onion around chicken. Sprinkle vegetables with 1 teaspoon olive oil and ¼ teaspoon salt. Roast until chicken is cooked through and vegetables are tender, 25–30 minutes. Sprinkle vegetables with chopped fresh dill.

**Crunchy Deviled Chicken
with Roasted Broccoli and Peppers**

Brussels Sprouts

THERE'S NO DOUBT THAT BRUSSELS SPROUTS HAVE gotten short shrift: Many of us see them on the Thanksgiving table and then not again for another year, which is a shame. Not only are these diminutive cabbages far more versatile than they're usually given credit for, they also boast an excellent nutritional profile. And if you or someone you know loathes Brussels sprouts, there's a good chance that improper cooking is the culprit.

CHOOSING & STORING

* Look for firm, uniformly sized Brussels sprouts with no (or minimal) browning at the base or yellowing of the outer leaves.

* Smaller sprouts will generally be more tender and sweeter.

* Take a pass on pale-green sprouts; the color may be a sign that the darker outer leaves have been stripped off to hide the signs of age or improper handling.

* Buy sprouts that are sold still clustered along their large, heavy stalk if you see them available. Not only does the stalk make a fabulous conversation piece, but the sprouts will keep longer and are likely to taste phenomenally fresh when you remove them to cook.

* Store sprouts wrapped first in a paper towel and then loosely in plastic.

GOOD FOR YOU

Brussels sprouts are a good source of folate, a B vitamin that's essential for healthy pregnancy.

COOK THEM RIGHT

* Rinse Brussels sprouts and remove any discolored outer leaves. Cut a thin sliver off the base of the sprouts' stems if they are browned.

* Scoring the bottom of each stem with an X will help heat penetrate the core of the sprout, making for more even cooking.

* Large sprouts (those as big as Ping Pong balls) should be halved before cooking; smaller, daintier ones can be left whole.

* Cook sprouts just until crisp-tender, no longer. A fork should meet just a little resistance when poked into the stem end of a properly cooked sprout.

* Don't like the cabbage smell of cooking Brussels sprouts? A few slices of red bell pepper added to the cooking or steaming water will help neutralize the aroma.

**Brussels Sprouts
with Orecchiette**

Roasted Brussels Sprouts and Carrots

Preheat oven to 450°F. Place 1 cup Brussels sprouts and ½ cup baby-cut carrots on small baking pan; drizzle with 1 teaspoon olive oil. Sprinkle with 1 minced garlic clove and pinch each salt and pepper. Roast until soft and browned, 12–15 minutes.

Brussels Sprout Slaw

Thinly slice 1 cup fresh Brussels sprouts. Toss with 2 tablespoons lemon juice, 1 teaspoon olive oil, 1 tablespoon shredded Romano cheese, and pinch cracked black pepper.

Brussels Sprouts with Orecchiette

Combine 1 cup halved Brussels sprouts with ¾ cup low-sodium fat-free chicken broth and pinch each salt and pepper in medium skillet. Cover and simmer until sprouts are tender, about 8 minutes. Stir in ½ cup cooked whole wheat orecchiette and sprinkle with 1 slice cooked crumbled turkey bacon.

CABE
CANTA
CAR
CAULIFI
CHER
COLLARD
CUCUM

Cabbage

IN SEASON **Year-round**

THINK YOU KNOW CABBAGE? MOST OF US ARE FAMILIAR
with head cabbages (**green, white, red,** and **Savoy**) since they serve
as the base for staple dishes like coleslaw, sauerkraut, and stuffed
cabbage. Less familiar are loose-leaf cabbages like **bok choy, Napa,**
and a myriad of sturdy to feathery cabbages popular in Asian
cuisines. The good news is that all the members of the *Brassica*
group share a spectacular nutritional profile, including compounds
that may help prevent a number of cancers.

CHOOSING & STORING

* Look for very dense heads of cabbage with glossy, crisp, tightly packed leaves. There should be no sign of browning at the base of the leaves.

* Loose-leaf cabbages like bok choy should have crisp, unblemished stems and soft, fresh-looking leaves.

* Cabbage is famous for keeping well; uncut head cabbage can be refrigerated, loosely wrapped in plastic, for weeks, while loose-leaf varieties like bok choy and choy sum will keep for 3 or 4 days.

PREPARE IT RIGHT

* Remove any curled, browned, or wilted outer leaves from cabbage.

* Rinse the outer leaves of head cabbages and all the leaves of loose-leaf cabbages; blot dry.

* For head cabbage, cut the entire head lengthwise into halves or quarters, then cut out and discard the thick, white inner core.

* Shred cabbage for slaws or salads on the large holes of a box grater or with the slicing blade of a food processor, or simply thinly slice with a sharp knife (preferable for loose-leaf cabbages like bok choy).

* To remove leaves whole for stuffing, do not cut the cabbage; submerge the entire head in a very large pot of boiling water and cook until the outer leaves are flexible, 2 to 3 minutes. Immediately drain, discard water, and cool the cabbage under cold running water. Leaves should peel off easily.

Cabbage

Baby bok choy

Small, loose heads with squat, pale green leaves and crunchy stems; sweet and mildly mustard-like flavor

BEST FOR
Salads, grilling, steaming, braising

GOOD TO KNOW
Very small heads are best cooked whole; heads over 6 inches long can be split before cooking

Bok choy

Tall heads with thick, juicy, ivory-colored stalks and tender, green or dark green leaves; sweet, mildly earthy flavor

BEST FOR
Salads, grilling, stir-frying, soups

GOOD TO KNOW
Leaves will cook faster than stems, so consider separating the two and adding stems first, leaves toward the end of cooking

Choy sum

Thick stems with tender, dark green leaves and small yellow flowers; earthy flavor

BEST FOR
Steaming, stir-frying, soups

GOOD TO KNOW
Prepare for cooking as you would broccoli rabe

Green

Dense, crisp, apple green heads; mild to strong cabbage flavor

BEST FOR
Salads, slaws, braising, stir-frying, stuffed leaves

GOOD TO KNOW
Excellent cut into thick wedges and braised

Napa

Glossy, loose heads of long, slightly crinkled leaves; mild to strong cabbage flavor

BEST FOR
Salads, slaws, stir-fries, soups, kimchi

GOOD TO KNOW
Also known as Chinese cabbage

Red

Dense, crisp, brilliant-purple or magenta heads; mild to strong cabbage flavor

BEST FOR
Salads, slaws, braising, stir-frying

GOOD TO KNOW
Cooking this cabbage with acidic ingredients like wine, vinegar, or lemon juice will help preserve its vibrant color

Savoy

Looser heads of crinkly, deep green leaves; mild flavor

BEST FOR
Salads, braising, stir-frying, stuffed leaves

GOOD TO KNOW
The attractive texture of the leaves makes them a favorite for stuffing

White

Dense, crisp, very pale green heads; very mild cabbage flavor

BEST FOR
Slaws, sauerkraut

GOOD TO KNOW
The classic cabbage for sauerkraut and pickling

Cabbage

KEEP COOKED CABBAGE SMELLING SWEET

Cabbage releases a variety of smelly sulfur compounds as it cooks. Boiling releases these compounds most dramatically, and the longer cabbage boils the smellier it gets. Minimize sulfurous odors with these tricks:

* Choose steaming, microwaving, or sautéing cabbage over boiling when possible.

* Add a few chunks of bread to the water when boiling cabbage to help lessen odors; toss the bread out when cooking is done.

* Try to keep cooking time to 5 minutes or less to reduce odors.

GOOD FOR YOU

Cabbage is rich in vitamin K and vitamin C, but its antioxidant content is what makes it one of the most promising vegetables for disease prevention. Red cabbage, in particular, contains an impressive concentration of antioxidants. Each variety of cabbage has a slightly different nutrient profile, so incorporate as many types into your diet as possible for optimum health benefits.

Cabbage and White Bean Soup

Combine 1 cup shredded Savoy cabbage, 1 cup fat-free low-sodium vegetable broth, 1 medium chopped tomato, 1 small sliced onion, ¼ cup rinsed, drained canned cannellini beans, and 2 minced garlic cloves in medium saucepan; bring to boil. Reduce heat and simmer, covered, until cabbage is tender, about 15 minutes.

Crunchy Slaw and Chicken Wrap

Toss together ½ cup shredded red cabbage, ½ cup sliced cooked chicken breast, 2 thinly sliced radishes, 1 tablespoon chopped fresh cilantro, and 2 teaspoons lime juice. Spoon into 1 small fat-free flour tortilla and roll up.

Bok Choy with Mushrooms and Noodles

Cook 1 cup sliced bok choy, ¼ pound small shiitake mushroom caps, and 1 teaspoon grated peeled fresh ginger in 1 teaspoon canola oil in skillet until tender, about 5 minutes. Add ¼ cup cooked whole wheat angel-hair pasta, ¼ cup fat-free low-sodium chicken broth, and 1 tablespoon low-sodium soy sauce to skillet; heat through. Sprinkle with 2 tablespoons sliced scallions.

**Bok Choy with
Mushrooms and Noodles**

Cantaloupe

IN SEASON **July to September**

SWEET, JUICY, AND DIVINELY AROMATIC—NOTHING beats a perfectly ripe cantaloupe for sheer fruit enjoyment. Dive into a half melon with a spoon, cut it into wedges to eat out of hand, or mix and match its luscious flavor with other fruits and savory ingredients.

CHOOSING & STORING

Selecting and storing a melon for peak flavor and deliciousness takes a little knowledge; melons harvested too early will never reach their potential.

* Look for pronounced netting on the skin with a background color of beige to golden and little or no green.

* Check that no stem is still attached to the melon; properly ripened melons "slip" from the vine, leaving only a slight indentation where they were attached. Also check that there is no bruising or mold here, a sign that the melon may already be too ripe.

* Finally, hold the dimpled blossom end a few inches from your nose and give it a sniff. A good cantaloupe should smell sweet and slightly musky. If you smell nothing, the chances are it was harvested too early to ever ripen; if you smell something fermented or sour, it's likely the melon is already spoiling.

* Cantaloupes will continue to ripen slightly if left on the counter for a few days, but if left out longer they may soften and ferment.

WHAT CHEFS KNOW

* Cantaloupe combines well with lime, hot chiles, almonds, hazelnuts, mint, cilantro, ham, balsamic vinegar, feta cheese, red onion, shrimp, and crab.

* A little lime juice or orange juice perks up the flavor of unripe cantaloupe.

* Overripe melons become mushy and watery, but if their flavor is still good (not sour or fermented) they're excellent for blending into smoothies.

* Should cantaloupe be served chilled or room temperature? It's your choice. Chilled cantaloupe is delightfully refreshing, although the melon's flavor and aroma will be more intense at room temperature.

GOOD FOR YOU

One cup of cantaloupe provides around 60 mg of vitamin C—that's about all you need of this antioxidant vitamin in a day.

3 PointsPlus value

Cantaloupe Cream Smoothie

Place ½ cup cubed peeled cantaloupe, ¼ cup fat-free vanilla frozen yogurt, 3 tablespoons orange juice, and 4 ice cubes in blender and puree until smooth.

3 PointsPlus value

Fiery Melon Mélange

Combine ½ cup cubed cantaloupe, ¼ cup cubed honeydew melon, and ¼ cup cubed seedless watermelon in medium bowl. Gently toss with 1 tablespoon lime juice, 1 tablespoon chopped fresh mint, 1 teaspoon honey, and ½ teaspoon minced seeded jalapeño pepper.

3 PointsPlus value

Melon and Strawberry Salad with Pickled Ginger

Toss 1 cup cubed cantaloupe with 1 cup sliced strawberries and 1 tablespoon finely chopped pickled ginger in medium bowl. Squirt with a little lime juice and a few grinds black pepper.

Carrots

IN SEASON **June to September**

CARROTS ARE AS DELICIOUS RAW AS THEY ARE COOKED, and so versatile that they're found in almost every cuisine around the world. They often play a supporting role in stocks, stews, salads, and sauces, but they're also delightful as the main event. Visit farmers' markets to find carrots at their flavorful, aromatic best. A real treat are sweet, tender **baby carrots,** harvested while still very small. Quite different, and not as flavorful, are bags of **"baby-cut,"** or **"cocktail,"** carrots, which are simply peeled, shaped sections of larger carrots.

CHOOSING & STORING

* Look for smooth, moist skins on carrots, a sign of freshness.

* Avoid overly large "horse carrots"; they're usually woody and tasteless.

* If carrots are sold with tops attached, the greens should be sprightly and green with no sign of yellowing or wilting. Remove the tops before storage as they will drain the carrots of moisture.

* Buy bagged, peeled baby-cut carrots carefully; sniff the bag first to make sure it smells fresh, not sour; then pinch a carrot through the bag to see that it feels firm and dry, not slimy.

* Consider buying organic since carrots are among the vegetables with the highest pesticide residues. Pesticides are concentrated in the skin, so peeling conventionally grown carrots is recommended even though it will decrease the vegetable's nutrient levels somewhat.

* Store carrots in a plastic bag in the refrigerator for up to a week.

DELICIOUS AT EVERY MEAL

Carrots are a dream in the kitchen: They're excellent raw, almost impossible to overcook, and work with just about every flavor palate we know. Try these sweet and savory tricks:

* Mix grated carrots with dried fruits and serve over yogurt or oatmeal.

* Grate raw carrots to add to slaws, salads, soups, pilaf, and even meat loaf or pasta sauce. They also enhance muffin, pancake, and other quick-bread batters. They'll even fit into many cookie and candy recipes.

* Use cooked pureed carrots as a base for soups, dips, or dressings.

* Cut carrots into sticks and serve with fat-free dressing, salsa, or mustard.

* Lay large carrots across the bottom of a roasting pan to make a flavorful, edible "rack" for a whole fish or a lean pork or beef roast.

Carrots

Spring Rolls with Ginger-Carrot Dipping Sauce

Whisk together 2 tablespoons carrot juice, 2 teaspoons rice vinegar, 1 teaspoon low-sodium soy sauce, and 1 teaspoon peeled and grated fresh ginger in small bowl. Dip 2 rice-paper wrappers in bowl of warm water until softened, about 1 minute. Transfer to work surface. Top center of each wrapper with ¼ cup shredded carrots, ¼ cup red bell pepper strips, and 1 tablespoon sliced scallion. Fold two opposite sides in, then roll up to enclose filling. Serve with dipping sauce.

Carrot Sticks with Maple-Spiced Yogurt

Combine ½ cup plain fat-free Greek yogurt, 1 teaspoon maple syrup, and ½ teaspoon ground cinnamon in small bowl. Serve with ½ cup carrot sticks.

Honey-Roasted Carrots with Orange and Thyme

Preheat oven to 450°F. Cut 1 small unpeeled orange into 6 wedges and place on small baking pan with 1 cup baby-cut carrots. Drizzle with 1 teaspoon honey and toss with 1 teaspoon chopped fresh thyme. Roast until soft and browned, about 10 minutes.

GOOD FOR YOU

One cup of carrots provides much more than the recommended daily dietary intake of vitamin A, making carrots the most powerful vegetable source for that health-protecting nutrient. They're also packed with B vitamins and are a good source of fiber.

**Spring Rolls with Ginger-Carrot
Dipping Sauce**

Cauliflower

THERE'S A LOT TO LOVE ABOUT CAULIFLOWER: NUTTY and sweet, it has a crunchy, pleasantly crumbly texture when raw but with cooking turns so velvety smooth that it's often used as a stand-in for mashed potatoes. Ivory heads are the norm, although **pale green, purple,** and **orange** varieties, identical in flavor, are sometimes available. More unusual (and quite expensive) is **baby cauliflower,** a diminutive head about the size of a tennis ball. A close cousin to cauliflower is the striking **Romanesco,** a lime green head with fantastically whorled florets.

CHOOSING & STORING

* Avoid cauliflower with brown or gray spotting, a sign of age or water damage.

* Look for heads that are very dense, with tightly clustered "curds."

* Green leaves at the base of the head should be crisp and fresh looking.

* Refrigerate cauliflower loosely wrapped in a paper or a plastic bag for no more than 2 to 3 days.

* Always store cauliflower stem side down to keep condensation from forming on the head and affecting its color or texture.

GOOD FOR YOU

Glucosinolates, the sulfur-containing compounds in cauliflower, may help protect against a number of diseases, including some cancers.

WHAT CHEFS KNOW

* Add some drama to dinner by boiling or steaming a head of cauliflower whole; simply cook until the core is just tender, place on a platter, and cut into wedges at the table.

* Roast cauliflower until it is lightly browned to make the most of its sweetness and nuttiness.

* Steam and puree cauliflower for a delectable alternative to mashed potatoes.

* Many people enjoy crunchy cauliflower raw in salads or on a crudité plate, although others find it too musty raw. If you belong to the latter group, blanch the florets in boiling water for just 60 seconds, cool under cold water, pat dry, and enjoy.

* Cauliflower is wonderful plain, but also has a great affinity for very strong flavors like cumin, curry, ginger, garlic, chiles, olives, capers, and blue cheese.

Roasted Cauliflower Tikka

Cauliflower Raita

Steam 1 cup cauliflower florets until crisp-tender, 4–5 minutes. Combine ½ cup plain fat-free yogurt, 2 tablespoons chopped fresh mint, ½ teaspoon ground cumin, and pinch each salt and pepper in medium bowl. Add cauliflower; toss gently to coat. Cover and refrigerate until chilled, about 30 minutes or up to 2 hours.

Sautéed Cauliflower with Apple and Leek

Cook ¼ cup thinly sliced leek and 1 minced garlic clove with 1 teaspoon olive oil in skillet until soft. Core and chop (but don't peel) ½ small Golden Delicious apple. Add apple to skillet with 1 cup cauliflower florets and pinch each salt and pepper. Cook, covered, until cauliflower and apple are tender, about 8 minutes

Roasted Cauliflower Tikka

Preheat oven to 425°F. Toss 2 cups cauliflower florets with 1 teaspoon olive oil, 1 teaspoon garam masala, ½ teaspoon ground cumin, ¼ teaspoon salt, and pinch red pepper flakes in large bowl. Spread cauliflower in small roasting pan. Roast, turning once, until cauliflower is tender, about 15 minutes.

Celery

IN SEASON Year-round

IF YOU THINK THERE'S ANYTHING PLAIN, LOWLY, OR too "diet-like" about celery you need to revisit this complex, versatile veggie. Not only does it deliver one of the best crunches in the vegetable kingdom, it also packs an outstandingly fresh, herbal flavor that's as good raw as it is cooked. It's worth savoring!

CHOOSING & STORING

* Try to buy celery with leaves attached; soft, unwilted leaves are a sign of freshness. If the tops have been lopped off, the ends should look freshly cut, not brown or dried out.

* Look for plump outer stalks that are very light green to yellow; avoid bunches with dark green and fibrous-looking stalks, which are likely to be bitter.

* Gently bend a stalk; fresh celery should be crisp and rigid, not rubbery, and should snap rather than curve.

* Store celery in the crisper section loosely wrapped in plastic for a week or more. Keep it away from the coldest part of the refrigerator; its high water content makes it likely to freeze.

* Buy organic celery when possible since it is one of the vegetables with the highest pesticide residues.

GOOD FOR YOU

Celery is a good source of vitamin K, which helps the body absorb calcium for bone health.

WHAT CHEFS KNOW

* Rinse celery stalks very well before using; rinsing will remove any dirt or grit trapped at the base of the stalks and will also help remove pesticides from nonorganic celery.

* Outer stalks are the most fibrous and have the most pronounced aniselike flavor, making them ideal for stocks, soups, and other long-cooked dishes. They may be peeled with a vegetable peeler to remove the toughest fibers.

* The tender inner stalks, known as the heart, are better for eating raw in salads, slaws, or crudités; they have a mild, extremely fresh flavor and excellent crispness.

* Don't overlook cooking a bunch of celery whole; it's a flavorful, meltingly tender side dish when braised in chicken or vegetable stock or roasted with a drizzle of olive oil or sesame oil and a sprinkle of sea salt.

Lemony Celery-Tuna Salad

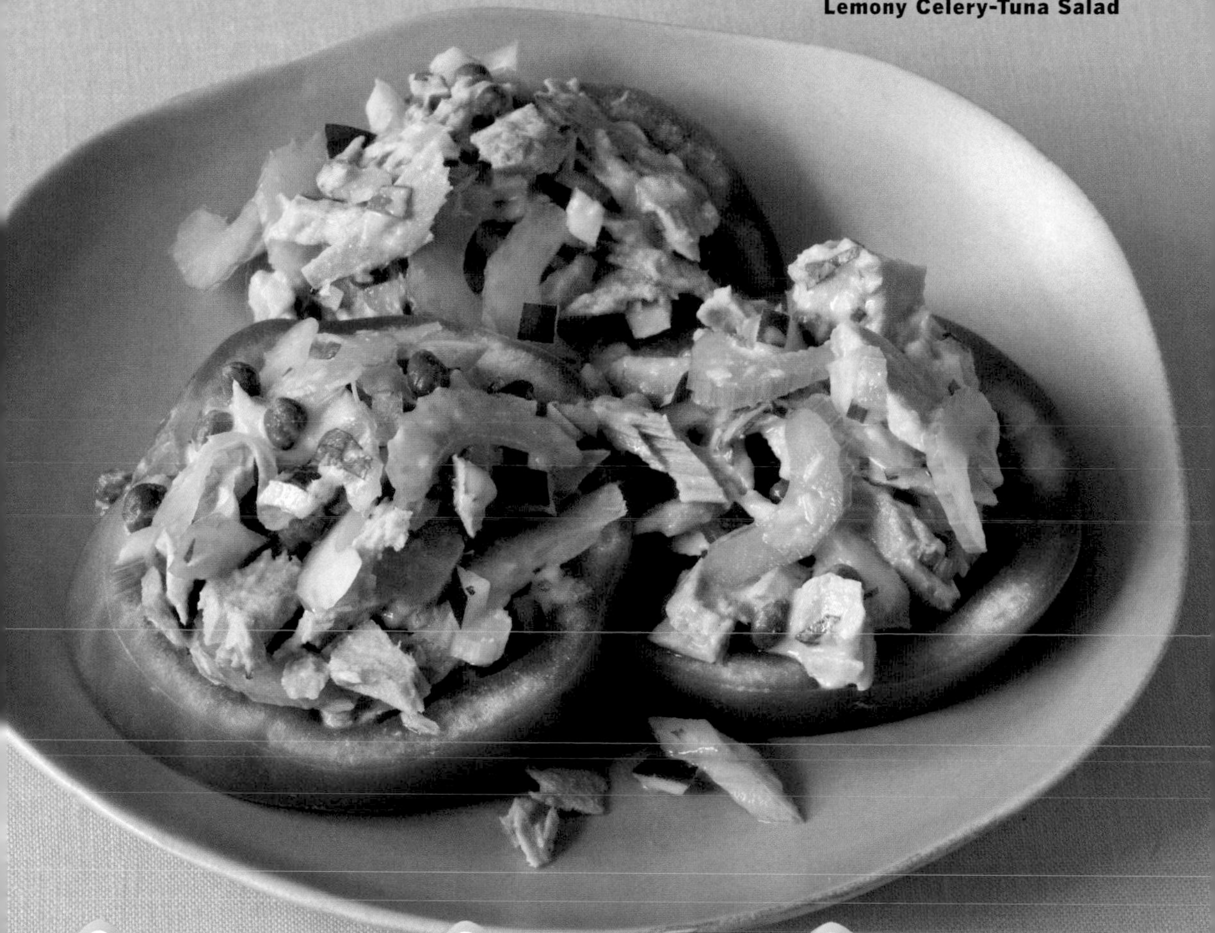

2 PointsPlus® value

Shaved Celery and Mushroom Salad

Thinly slice 2 medium celery stalks and toss in medium bowl with ½ cup thinly sliced cremini mushrooms, 1 tablespoon white balsamic vinegar, 1 teaspoon olive oil, and a sprinkling of cracked black pepper.

3 PointsPlus® value

Lemony Celery-Tuna Salad

Stir ½ cup drained canned tuna (packed in water) with ¼ cup sliced celery, 1 tablespoon diced red onion, 1 tablespoon capers, and 2 teaspoons chopped fresh tarragon in medium bowl. Whisk together 1 tablespoon lemon juice, 1 teaspoon Dijon mustard, and ¼ teaspoon salt in small bowl. Gently stir into tuna mixture. Serve on 2–3 tomato slices.

3 PointsPlus® value

Celery and Quinoa Salad with Pears and Almonds

Toss 1 cup chopped celery, 1 small chopped Asian pear, ¼ cup cooked quinoa, and 1 tablespoon rice vinegar in medium bowl. Sprinkle with 1 teaspoon slivered almonds.

Cherries

IN SEASON June to August

VIBRANTLY FLAVORED, BRILLIANTLY COLORED, AND AS shiny as a summer smile, cherries are one of the most anticipated fruits of the year. The majority of the cherries that flood our markets each June and July are **Bing** cherries—deep red, exceptionally juicy, and outstanding for both snacking and baking. You may also see a number of yellow varieties that sport just a spot of red blush, including **Rainier** and **Queen Anne**; these tend to be milder than Bings but are also excellent for snacking and baking. Small, soft **sour cherries** are sometimes available and are prized for baking and jam making but too tart for snacking.

CHOOSING & STORING

* It pays to select your cherries one at a time; underripe, overripe, or damaged fruit will always disappoint, so choose carefully.

* Pick fruit that is very shiny, deep in color (a sign of ripeness), and completely free of brown bruising or blemishes.

* Look for plump, bouncy cherries; very firm cherries may have been harvested too early, and soft ones (other than sour varieties) may be overripe.

* Choose the biggest fruits. Cherries gain most of their flavor and sugar content in the last days before harvesting, so larger usually means tastier.

* Select cherries still attached to the stem; they will remain fresher longer.

* Refrigerate cherries in a plastic bag for up to 3 days. You can also freeze them (pitted or unpitted) for up to 6 months.

WHAT CHEFS KNOW

* Make the most out of cherry season by investing in a pitter. You can also poke the pits out with a plastic drinking straw, but the straw will start to bend after a few dozen cherries.

* Choose yellow cherry varieties and you'll save yourself from the dark, staining juices of darker cherries. Yellow cherries are lovely in salads.

* Cherries pair beautifully with the flavors of cheeses, tarragon, thyme, black pepper, fennel, almonds, apples, blueberries, brandy, chocolate, yogurt, and vanilla.

* Cherries—sour or sweet—make an exceptional sauce for pork, poultry, salmon, and game.

* A small amount of almond extract will brighten and heighten the flavor of cherries.

Cherries

Cherry and Smoked Turkey Wrap

Spread 1 tablespoon fat-free mayonnaise over 1 small fat-free tortilla.
Top with 2 (¾-ounce) slices smoked turkey breast, ¼ cup cucumber slices,
1 sliced scallion, and 2 tablespoons chopped pitted fresh cherries; roll up.

Cherry Tea Sandwich

Mix 1 tablespoon reduced-fat cream cheese and 1 tablespoon fresh pitted
and chopped cherries in small bowl. Cut 1 slice pumpernickel bread in half
diagonally. Spread cream cheese mixture over one half. Top with ½ ounce
trimmed watercress and other half of bread slice.

Cherry-Almond Freeze

Place ¼ cup pitted fresh or frozen cherries (no need to thaw if frozen), ½ cup
fat-free vanilla frozen yogurt, and ½ teaspoon almond extract in blender and
puree until smooth. Spoon into a small bowl and top with pinch freshly
grated nutmeg and 1 teaspoon sliced almonds.

GOOD FOR YOU

Cherries are one of the top antioxidant-containing foods and a valuable
source of fiber, vitamin C, and potassium, a nutrient that may help decrease
the risk of heart disease and stroke.

Cherry-Almond Freeze

Collard Greens

IN SEASON December to April

BIG FLAVOR, BIG TEXTURE, AND BIG NUTRITION—
collards have a lot to offer! They're one of the South's staple
vegetables and are quickly becoming a favorite nationwide.
Cook them long and slow (for hours even) until they practically
melt, or give them shorter, higher heat to retain more of their
original color and texture; the choice is yours.

CHOOSING & STORING

* Look for crisp, dark-green to blue-green leaves with no sign of wilting or browning.

* Take a pass on leaves with holes or rough edges, both of which can be a sign of insect damage.

* Choose bunches with thinner stalks and small ribs if you can; thick stalks and ribs will have to be stripped out and discarded before cooking, so you won't be eating everything you paid for.

* Store collards in a loosely closed plastic bag in the coldest part of your refrigerator for no more than a few days.

* Collards shrink dramatically during cooking, so you'll need about 1/3 pound fresh greens to yield a 1/2-cup serving of cooked greens.

WHAT CHEFS KNOW

* Collards have lots of flavor on their own, but some tasty additions include garlic, onion, red pepper, cider vinegar, and hot sauce.

* Collards are one of the sturdiest greens; you can steam, braise, or sauté them for minutes or hours. If you're new to collard cooking, you may want to stop and taste them every 5 or 10 minutes to find the texture you like best.

* Substitute collards for other sturdy greens like kale, Swiss chard, or mustard greens, but remember that collards may require slightly more cooking time.

GOOD FOR YOU

Collard greens are a good vegetable source of calcium and vitamin C.

Hoppin' John Chopped Salad

Hoppin' John Chopped Salad

2 PointsPlus value

Whisk together 2 tablespoons apple cider vinegar, 1 chopped shallot, 1 teaspoon Dijon mustard, and pinch salt in medium bowl. Toss with 1 cup chopped trimmed collard greens, ½ diced bell pepper, and ¼ cup drained canned black-eyed peas.

Green Gumbo

2 PointsPlus value

Combine 1 ½ cups fat-free low-sodium chicken broth, 1 cup chopped trimmed collard greens, ½ small chopped onion, ¼ cup fresh or frozen sliced okra, and 1 minced garlic clove in medium saucepan; bring to boil. Reduce heat and simmer, covered, until vegetables are tender, about 15 minutes.

Maple-Glazed Collards

2 PointsPlus value

Cook 1 sliced scallion with 1 teaspoon olive oil in skillet until tender. Add 1 cup trimmed and chopped collard greens and cook until wilted, 4–5 minutes. Stir in 1 teaspoon maple syrup and pinch each salt and pepper; cook until collards are tender and glazed, about 5 minutes longer.

Corn

IN SEASON **July to September**

A NORTH AMERICAN ORIGINAL, CORN IS TODAY THE world's second most widely grown crop after rice. **Sweet corn,** of course, is the variety we cook as a vegetable (though it's technically a grain), and corn on the cob routinely tops lists of Americans' all-time favorite vegetables.

CHOOSING & STORING

Buying the freshest corn on the cob will really pay off. Its sugars begin to turn to starch the moment it's picked, leaving once delectably sweet, tender kernels dense and tasteless within a few days. Buy corn from a farmers' market or vegetable stand if possible; it's likely to have been picked that day.

* Look for ears snugly wrapped in moist (not dried out) bright green husks.

* The silk at the tip of the ear should be golden or golden brown; it should look fresh and glossy, not wilted.

* Peel back the very tip of the husk if you can; look for plump, shiny kernels that are packed along the ear in neat rows.

* Refrigerate corn loosely wrapped in a plastic or paper bag for no more than a day; leaving it in the husk will help preserve freshness.

* Wondering if off-season corn on the cob from your supermarket is any good? You may see it packed 3 or 4 ears to a tray, usually with the husks removed to hide signs of age. It's liable to be unexceptional at best, but if frozen corn kernels just won't do it you can give it a try. Adding a few teaspoons of sugar to your cooking water may sweeten its flavor.

COOK IT RIGHT

Cooking times for corn on the cob vary widely, depending on the number of ears, freshness, variety, and your personal preference.

Boil It Choose a pot large enough to hold the number of ears you're cooking plus enough water to cover them all by at least 2 inches. Bring the water to a rolling boil, add the corn, cover, and cook until the kernels brighten and plump slightly and are just tender, 1 to 6 minutes after the water comes back to a boil. Drain and serve.

Steam It Pull down (but do not break off) the husks and remove the silk. Smooth the husks back over the ear and tie the top with a piece of kitchen string. Steam over simmering water, covered, until the kernels feel just slightly tender when you press on the husk, 5 to 10 minutes. *Continued* »

Corn

Grill It Pull down (but do not break off) the husks and remove the silk. Smooth the husks back over the ear, tie the top with a piece of kitchen string, and soak in a large bowl or tub of cold water for at least 30 minutes and up to an hour. Grill over medium coals until the kernels are softened and the husks are slightly charred, 10 to 20 minutes.

Try It Raw Very fresh, very sweet corn is excellent raw in salads, slaws, and salsas. To remove the kernels from a husked ear, begin by slicing off the stem end so that the ear stands level; then hold the tip with one hand and use a knife to cut downward on the ear, removing 3 or 4 rows of kernels with each cut.

GOOD FOR YOU

In addition to a wealth of important B vitamins, sweet corn contains fiber and vitamin C.

Sweet Corn Hash

Cook ½ cup fresh or frozen corn kernels, ½ diced red bell pepper, ¼ cup diced zucchini, and 2 tablespoons sliced scallions with 1 teaspoon olive oil in skillet until crisp-tender, about 6 minutes. Add ½ cup halved cherry tomatoes and ¼ cup diced lean ham. Cook until tomatoes just begin to soften, 2–3 minutes. Stir in 1 tablespoon chopped fresh tarragon.

Velvety Corn Soup with Edamame

Cook 1 minced garlic clove, 1 teaspoon peeled and minced fresh ginger, and ½ minced seeded jalapeño pepper with 1 teaspoon oil in skillet until fragrant, about 1 minute. Add 1½ cups fat-free low-sodium chicken broth, ½ cup fresh or frozen corn kernels, and ¼ cup frozen shelled edamame; simmer until corn and edamame are tender, about 8 minutes. Sprinkle with chives.

Corn on the "Cobb" Salad

Spread 2 cups chopped romaine lettuce on plate. Arrange ½ cup diced cooked turkey breast, ½ cup halved cherry tomatoes, and ½ cup cooked fresh corn kernels in rows on top of lettuce. Drizzle with 2 tablespoons fat-free blue cheese dressing and sprinkle with 1 slice crumbled crisp-cooked turkey bacon.

Corn on the "Cobb" Salad

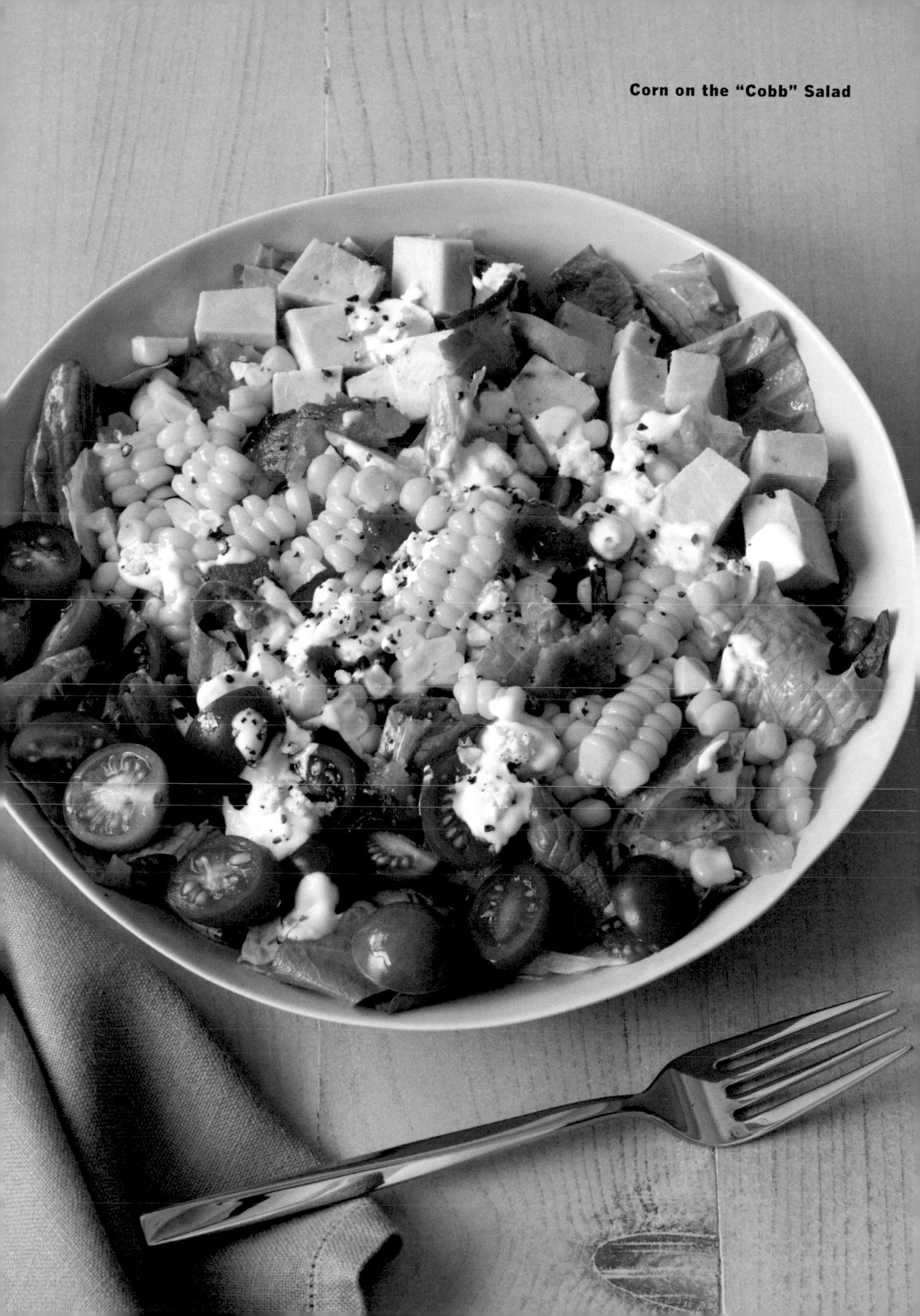

Cucumbers

IN SEASON June to September

GARDEN, OR **SLICING**, CUCUMBERS ARE WHAT YOU'RE most likely to see stacked at your supermarket. Preferable in the summer months are smaller, crunchier **Kirby,** or **pickling,** cucumbers with bumpy skins, sweet flesh, and small seeds. Greenhouse-grown, super-long **hothouse,** or **English,** cucumbers are conveniently thin-skinned and virtually seedless; their flavor is unremarkable, but consistent year-round quality makes them a good choice in the off-season. Less common but also a good choice out of season are small, sweet **Lebanese,** or **Middle Eastern,** cucumbers.

CHOOSING & STORING

Be picky when it comes to cucumbers; bad ones can be bitter, watery, and not worth buying.

* Inspect a cucumber's skin to make sure it's firm, unblemished, and taut (not wrinkled).

* Check the ends closely for yellowing, a sign of overmaturity.

* Select smaller, thinner specimens of whatever variety you're buying, and you'll usually be rewarded with superior flavor and crisper texture.

* Cucumbers dehydrate quickly, so refrigerate them for no more than a few days in a loosely sealed plastic bag. Since they're susceptible to cold damage, keep them in a warmer part of your refrigerator.

GOOD FOR YOU

Cucumbers are a good source of vitamin K, essential for bone health and proper blood clotting.

PEELING & SEEDING

* Always peel the tough, bitter, and often waxed skin of garden cucumbers.

* Soups will be smoother if you use peeled cucumbers, but you may miss the skin's green color in the finished product; use varieties with thin, sweet skins and you can compromise by leaving the skin on half the amount.

* The skins of hothouse and Lebanese cucumbers are thin and delicious, and look particularly attractive with this trick: Run a dinner fork down the length of the cucumber, pressing so that the tines just stripe the surface; continue all around the cucumber and then slice or cut it as desired.

* Cucumber seeds become larger and more bitter with age; do a taste test to see if the ones in your cucumber should be removed.

* Seed cucumbers by splitting them in half lengthwise and scraping a teaspoon down the center.

**Cucumber and
Salmon Sandwiches**

Cucumber Kimchi

Combine ½ medium seeded
and chopped cucumber, ½ cup
shredded carrot, and 2 chopped
scallions in small bowl. Bring
2 tablespoons rice vinegar,
1 teaspoon peeled and minced
fresh ginger, 1 minced garlic
clove, ½ teaspoon sugar, and
pinch red pepper flakes to boil
in saucepan. Let cool 5 minutes, then pour over cucumber
mixture. Chill at least 1 hour.

Cucumber-Pimiento
Cheese Canapés

Combine ½ cup softened
fat-free cream cheese with
1 tablespoon chopped pimien-
tos and 1 tablespoon chopped
fresh basil in small bowl. Spoon
1 tablespoon on each of 8
(½-inch-thick) slices hothouse
or English cucumber. Garnish
each with 1 small basil leaf.

Cucumber and
Salmon Sandwiches

Combine ¼ cup canned salmon
with 1 tablespoon fat-free
mayonnaise and 1 teaspoon
each grated onion, chopped
fresh dill, and lemon juice in
small bowl. Spoon mixture on
1 slice reduced-calorie whole
grain bread. Top with ¼ cup
sliced Kirby cucumber.

Eggplant

IN SEASON **July to October**

EGGPLANT TURNS FAMOUSLY RICH AND MEATY WITH cooking, making it a favorite across the globe and particularly beloved of vegetarians. Hundreds of varieties are grown worldwide, although by far the most common in the United States is the large deep-purple **Italian** eggplant. Smaller varieties also abound, including slender **Japanese** eggplants, **white** eggplants in a number of shapes and sizes, and **baby** eggplants in shades of purple, lavender, or green and white. The good news is that all varieties have similar cooking qualities, making experimentation easy.

CHOOSING & STORING

Forget about gender when selecting eggplants; despite much talk, there is no such thing as a "male" or "female" since all eggplants are self-pollinating. A body of lore suggests that females are more likely to be seedy and bitter, but both of these characteristics are the result of variety and overmaturity, not gender. Concentrate on selecting young, fresh eggplants, and you're likely to be happy with their flavor.

* Look for eggplants with taut, glossy skin without brown spots or indentations.

* Check the stem end; the green cap here should be free of mold or brown coloring.

* Give each eggplant a lift; heaviness for its size is a sign that the flesh is moist and dense, not dry and seedy (and possibly bitter).

* Store eggplants unwrapped in a cool, dry place or wrapped loosely in plastic in the warmest part of the refrigerator.

* Fresher is always better with eggplants, so use them within 2 or 3 days

TO SALT OR NOT TO SALT

Salting was once considered mandatory to remove bitter juices from eggplant, but you're unlikely to find a bitter specimen these days unless it's past its prime. What salting will do is pull out some moisture and reduce the sponginess of the flesh, resulting in less oil absorption and perhaps better texture after cooking. Can you skip the salting step? The answer is probably yes; reducing the amount of oil the eggplant comes in contact with during cooking is a better way to decrease fat absorption, and proper cooking is the most effective way to ensure good texture. If you do decide to salt, here's an easy method:

* Slice your eggplant into the desired thickness, or cut into chunks.

* Sprinkle generously with kosher salt and place in a colander in the sink or over a bowl.

* Let the eggplant sit for 30 minutes, then pat dry.

Eggplant

Mediterranean Eggplant Wrap

Cut 1 small (4-ounce) eggplant crosswise on diagonal into 4 slices and spray with nonstick spray. Grill over medium-high heat in grill pan sprayed with nonstick spray until soft and brown, about 4 minutes per side. Spread 1 teaspoon prepared pesto on 1 small fat-free flour tortilla. Top with eggplant, ¼ cup arugula, and 2 tomato slices and roll up.

Pasta with Eggplant Puttanesca

Cook 1 cup cubed eggplant in skillet sprayed with nonstick spray until soft and brown, about 8 minutes. Add 1 cup canned diced tomatoes, 4 pitted and chopped kalamata olives, and 1 teaspoon capers; bring to boil. Cover and simmer 10 minutes. Stir in ¼ cup cooked whole wheat bow tie pasta and 2 tablespoons chopped fresh basil.

Tandoori Eggplant

Preheat broiler. Combine ¼ cup plain fat-free Greek yogurt, 1 tablespoon chopped fresh mint, 1 minced garlic clove, ½ teaspoon ground cumin, and pinch salt in small bowl. Cut 2 small (4-ounce) eggplants lengthwise in half; brush with yogurt mixture. Place in small baking pan and broil until browned and bubbly, about 4 minutes on each side. Top eggplant with 1 chopped tomato, 2 tablespoons crumbled reduced-fat feta cheese, and 1 tablespoon chopped fresh mint.

GOOD FOR YOU

Eggplant contains modest amounts of protein, fiber, and other major nutrients, but it's worth adding to your diet for its disease-fighting properties. In particular, eggplant skin contains anthocyanins, antioxidants that may help prevent heart disease and some cancers.

Tandoori Eggplant

Fennel

FENNEL'S THICK, CRISP, BUNCHING STEMS MAY REMIND you of celery, and both vegetables are members of the aromatic Apiaceae family, a family which includes anise, parsley, and dill. Fennel has a distinctive licorice-like flavor and feathery fronds that make a superb garnish. It's one of the few vegetables that come into season in deep autumn, making it an excellent ingredient to explore as the rest of the harvest fades out.

CHOOSING & STORING

* Look for pure white bulbs topped by abundant dark green fronds that show no sign of wilting.

* Select smaller bulbs for salads and other raw uses, as they are milder and slightly more tender.

* Choose larger bulbs for cooking; they will halve or quarter more easily, and their stronger flavor and denser texture will be mellowed with heat.

* Store fennel loosely in a plastic bag in the refrigerator crisper for 3 to 4 days.

GOOD FOR YOU

Fennel is one of the best vegetable sources of vitamin C. One bulb contains 28 mg, almost half the recommended daily dose.

WHAT CHEFS KNOW

* Raw fennel adds outstanding crunch and flavor to salads, slaws, and salsas. Try it in tuna salad, Waldorf salad, or anywhere else you would use raw celery.

* Cooked fennel is sweet, mild, and meltingly tender. Halve or quarter bulbs and grill, roast, steam, or braise; dice or thinly slice and add to soups, stews, or sautés.

* Fennel will begin to brown an hour or so after being cut; toss it with lemon juice or an acidic dressing to keep it white.

* Fennel goes brilliantly with the flavors of citrus, apple, tomato, anchovies, olives, almonds, walnuts, tangy cheeses, seafood, and wine.

Fennel Tabbouleh

Fennel Sticks with Orange Mayonnaise

Combine ¼ cup fat-free mayonnaise, 1 tablespoon orange juice, and 1 teaspoon grated orange zest in small bowl. Cut ½ medium fennel bulb lengthwise into ½-inch pieces and serve with the dip.

Fennel Tabbouleh

Combine ½ cup each cooked bulgur wheat, chopped fennel, and halved cherry tomatoes with 2 tablespoons minced red onion, 1 tablespoon chopped fresh mint, 1 tablespoon lemon juice, 1 teaspoon olive oil, and pinch each salt and pepper. Toss to mix well.

Fennel Salad with Orange and Arugula

Thinly slice ½ medium fennel bulb. Toss with 1 tablespoon lemon juice in medium bowl. Add 2 cups baby arugula, 1 small diced peeled orange, 1 teaspoon olive oil, and pinch each salt and pepper.

Grapefruit

IN SEASON **November to June**

GENEROUS SIZE, LEGENDARY JUICINESS, AND A SUNNY sweet-tart flavor tempered by a hint of bitterness make grapefruit a favorite winter citrus. Better yet, they seem to have the ability to make just about any food they come in contact with taste fresher, so enjoy them in salads, salsas, and seafood and poultry dishes. Most grapefruit are classified as either **white, pink,** or **red** (also called **ruby**), depending on the color of their flesh. White grapefruit is likely to be tarter and have more seeds than pink or red, but can be excellently juicy and flavorful too.

CHOOSING & STORING

* Look for skins that are smooth and supple with no signs of drying, wrinkling, or bruising.

* Avoid grapefruit that look like they have thick, puffy skins; these fruits have a lot of inedible pith and are generally less flavorful and juicy than thin-skinned varieties.

* Russeting, or browning, on the skin will not affect flavor or quality.

* Store grapefruit at room temperature for up to 1 week or loosely wrapped in the refrigerator for 2 to 3 weeks.

GOOD FOR YOU

A small red grapefruit packs about 48 mg of vitamin C—nearly the recommended daily dose—plus the antioxidant lycopene, which has been linked to several health benefits.

PREPARATION TIPS

The challenge: Removing all the bitter pith and tough membranes to enjoy grapefruit's succulent sections. Try these strategies:

* **Easy peeling grapefruit** Bring a saucepan of water to a boil. Drop in a grapefruit, remove the pan from the heat, cover, and let the grapefruit sit in the water for 5 minutes. Remove the fruit from the water, let it cool a few minutes, then peel—all the pith should come away with the skin.

* **Grapefruit sections for salads and salsas** Cut thin slices from the top and bottom of a fruit. Set it on a cutting board and cut down along the curve of the fruit, removing all the peel and pith and cutting all the way to the flesh. Now hold the whole skinless fruit over a bowl and cut along the membranes to release each segment, letting the segments and any juice drop into the bowl.

Grapefruit Brûlé

With small knife, loosen segments from ½ small grapefruit, freeing them from membrane. Mix together 1 teaspoon packed brown sugar, 1 teaspoon softened butter, and ¼ teaspoon cinnamon. Sprinkle over grapefruit. Broil until browned, 3–4 minutes.

Grapefruit-Shrimp Cocktail

Toss ½ small sectioned grapefruit with ½ cup drained and sliced canned hearts of palm and 2 tablespoons chopped mint. Mound onto 3 large radicchio leaves; top with 4 large cooked and peeled shrimp and drizzle with 1 tablespoon fat-free lime vinaigrette.

Chicken with Ruby Red Relish

Toss segments from ½ small red grapefruit with ½ small diced mango, 2 tablespoons chopped basil, 1 tablespoon minced red onion, ½ teaspoon honey, and pinch salt. Cook 1 (4-ounce) skinless, boneless chicken breast in skillet sprayed with nonstick spray until opaque in center, 2–3 minutes per side. Serve with relish.

Grapefruit-Shrimp Cocktail

Grapes

IN SEASON **September and October**

THOUSANDS OF GRAPE VARIETIES ARE CULTIVATED worldwide, the vast majority for making wine, vinegar, jelly, and raisins. Grapes sold for snacking are known as **table grapes** and are loosely classified as green, red, or black. Although seedless varieties are overwhelmingly popular, purists insist that seeded grapes are superior in flavor; have fun tasting both and decide for yourself. Do look out for two delicious, complexly flavored seeded varieties available in the fall: **Concord,** a native grape with a tart and musky flavor, and **Muscat,** an ancient grape with very juicy, honey-sweet flesh.

CHOOSING & STORING

* Look for grapes in bunches with the fruit still firmly attached to the stem—a sign of freshness. Individual grapes should be plump, with taut skin and no wrinkling; a powdery finish known as "bloom" on the skin of some varieties is a sign of freshness and careful handling.

* Grapes do not ripen further after picking; those harvested too early will be hard (not plump and juicy), small for their variety, and more sour than sweet.

* Taste a grape before buying if you can—it's the best way to judge if the fruit was properly ripened and matches your preference for flavor and texture.

* Store grapes at room temperature for a day or two; refrigerate them for up to a week wrapped loosely in a plastic bag or in the perforated plastic bag they came in.

* Grapes are one of the fruits with the most residual pesticides, so rinse them thoroughly before eating. Better yet, buy organic grapes if you can.

TASTE TIPS

* Make grapes a dessert worthy of company by mounding bunches of different varieties on a platter. Choose contrasting colors, shapes, and sizes for dramatic appeal, and include a pair of small scissors or special grape sheers so that guests can help themselves to a few clusters.

* Grapes are wonderful when roasted along with pork and poultry. The longer they roast, the softer they get, so add them when no more than 30 minutes of roasting time remains unless you want them to turn to mush (which is tasty too!).

* Freeze grapes for an icy treat: Cut small clusters from a bunch of grapes, rinse and pat dry, place on sheet pan and freeze until solid. Transfer to a freezer-safe bag and freeze up to 3 months. *Continued »*

Grapes

* Grapes are fantastic in creamy salads like tuna salad, chicken salad, and salmon salad and an excellent addition to tossed salads; halve them to make spearing them with a fork easier.

* Grapes and mild cheeses are a favorite combination. Take this duo way beyond the cheese plate: Toss hot pasta with grapes and low-fat feta, blue cheese, or farmer's cheese; add halved grapes to your next grilled cheese sandwich; or try a goat cheese pizza topped with grapes, walnuts, and arugula.

GOOD FOR YOU

Grapes contain a rich mixture of nutrient compounds that may help protect against heart disease, some cancers, and a number of other diseases associated with aging. You've probably heard of the health benefits associated with drinking red wine, and grapes contain many of the same antioxidants, including quercetin and resveratrol. Most of this good stuff is concentrated in the skins of dark-colored grapes, so choose red or black grapes and don't peel them.

Green Grape Gazpacho

Puree 1 medium peeled and chopped kiwifruit, ½ cup seedless green grapes, ¼ cup cubed honeydew melon, grated zest and juice of ½ lime, 1 tablespoon chopped fresh mint, and 1 teaspoon honey in blender until smooth. Cover and refrigerate until chilled.

Grape Salad with Goat Cheese and Pistachios

Combine ¾ cup halved seedless grapes, ½ cored and sliced red pear, and 1 tablespoon white balsamic vinegar in bowl. Sprinkle with 1 tablespoon crumbled soft goat cheese and 1 teaspoon chopped pistachios.

Crunchy Grape and Turkey Salad Roll

Toss ½ cup halved seedless grapes, ¼ cup cubed cooked turkey breast, ¼ cup diced celery, 1 tablespoon plain fat-free Greek yogurt, and 2 teaspoons chopped fresh tarragon in medium bowl. Serve in 1 light whole wheat hot dog roll.

Crunchy Grape and
Turkey Salad Roll

Green Beans

YOU MAY HAVE HEARD GREEN BEANS CALLED "STRING beans," a holdover from the days when most varieties had a tough, fibrous string running the length of the pod. Most green beans today are bred to be stringless, so removing this fiber ("stringing") is now a thing of the past. In addition to green beans, look for pale yellow **wax beans,** which are almost identical in taste and cooking qualities but add a lovely color contrast when mixed with darker ingredients (or with green beans). Also look out for slim, tender **haricots verts,** a delicate and delicious variety that needs just a minute or two of steaming or boiling.

CHOOSING & STORING

* Look for straight, smooth, vibrantly colored beans without wrinkling. The tips of the beans should look sprightly, not browned or tired.

* Fresh beans should be crisp and should snap rather than bend.

* Green beans should smell fresh and faintly grassy; those with no aroma at all may be past their prime.

* If you can see bumps where the bean's seeds lie in the pod, you can be sure the bean is too mature and will be tough and bland, not tender and sweet.

* Refrigerate green beans in a paper bag or loosely closed plastic bag for 2 to 3 days.

GOOD FOR YOU

One cup of cooked green beans delivers a heart-healthy 4 g of fiber.

TASTE TIPS

* Add a pinch of sugar to the cooking water to sweeten green beans, particularly those that might be a little past their prime.

* Green beans are excellent on a crudités platter. For best color and flavor, blanch the beans by cooking them in a large pot of boiling water for 30 seconds, draining, and immediately cooling them in a bowl of cold water.

* Acidic ingredients like vinegar or lemon juice will turn beans from bright green to dull khaki. The color change won't affect the beans' flavor, but if you want them to keep their vibrant color, add acids or vinaigrettes just before serving.

* Green beans go particularly well with citrus fruits, nuts, fennel, tomatoes, onions, garlic, ginger, olives, feta and Parmesan cheeses, soy sauce, cumin, and curry.

Green Bean Minestra

Asian Green Bean Salad

3 PointsPlus© value

Thinly slice 1 (3-ounce) head baby bok choy and toss in bowl with 1 cup steamed sliced green beans, ¼ cup chopped fresh cilantro, 1 tablespoon low-sodium soy sauce, 1 teaspoon toasted sesame oil, and pinch red pepper flakes.

Green Bean Minestra

3 PointsPlus© value

Sauté 1 minced garlic clove and 1 small chopped tomato in 1 teaspoon olive oil in saucepan until soft, about 5 minutes. Add 1½ cups fat-free low-sodium chicken broth, ½ cup sliced green beans, ½ cup sliced zucchini, and ½ cup baby spinach; bring to boil. Cover and simmer until vegetables are tender, 10–12 minutes. Sprinkle with 1 teaspoon grated Parmesan cheese.

Green Bean and Potato Salad

4 PointsPlus© value

Cut 1 small cooked (unpeeled) red potato into cubes and combine with 1 cup steamed green beans in medium bowl. Toss with 1 small chopped tomato, ¼ thinly sliced red onion, 2 tablespoons chopped fresh dill, 1 teaspoon olive oil, ½ teaspoon dried oregano, and pinch salt.

HONE
JI
KAL
KIWI

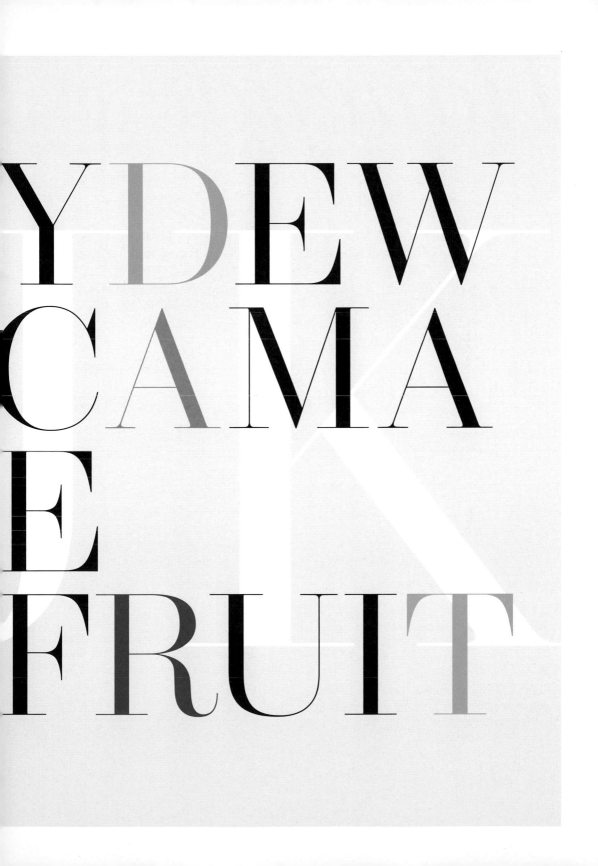

Honeydew

IN SEASON July to October

OH, HONEYDEW! A PERFECTLY RIPE HONEYDEW IS ONE of the sweetest of all melons, with crisp, juicy flesh and a lightly floral aroma. A high water content makes it a particularly refreshing treat and an excellent base for drinks, cold soups, and sorbet or granita. Look out for a few less common but equally delicious melons closely related to honeydew, including fragrant **galia** melons and supersweet **canary** melons.

CHOOSING & STORING

* Select large honeydews with smooth, unblemished skins.

* Press the stem end of a melon; it should give slightly when the fruit is ripe.

* You can also sniff the stem end of the melon to gauge ripeness. It should have a light floral aroma when it's ready for eating. If it smells very strongly fruity or sour, it may be overripe.

* Honeydews continue to ripen after picking, so leave them out on your kitchen counter for a few days if yours seems under ripe.

* Leaving the seeds in a halved melon for storage will help keep the fruit moist.

GOOD FOR YOU

One cup of diced honeydew contains a healthy 31 mg of vitamin C and 388 mg of potassium, a nutrient linked to heart health.

TASTE TIPS

* The very mild flavor and floral aroma of honeydews is best savored when the fruit is at room temperature, not chilled.

* Perfectly ripe honeydew needs no accompaniment, but if yours seems to be lacking in flavor you can sprinkle it with a little lime juice, orange juice, apple juice, or port. A little mint makes a flavorful garnish too.

* Fill a halved melon with shrimp salad, chicken salad, rice salad, cottage cheese, or frozen yogurt.

* Honeydew makes excellent smoothies and coolers; simply puree the flesh in a blender with lemon or lime or a sweet fruit juice to taste. You can strain the mixture for a smooth drink or simply pour into glasses; for a particularly cooling treat, pour it into ice-pop molds.

Honeydew, Avocado, and Pepita Salad

3 PointsPlus® value

Honeydew-Cucumber Smoothie

Place ¼ cup peeled, seeded, and chopped cucumber in blender with ½ cup peeled and diced honeydew, ½ cup white grape juice, and 1 tablespoon chopped fresh mint and puree with 2 ice cubes.

4 PointsPlus® value

Honeydew Melon and Sorbet Parfait

With melon baller, scoop out enough melon balls from ½ small honeydew to make 1 cup. Spoon melon balls into goblet or wine glass; sprinkle with 1 teaspoon lime juice. Top with ¼ cup coconut sorbet and sprinkle with grated zest of ½ lime.

5 PointsPlus® value

Honeydew, Avocado, and Pepita Salad

Whisk together 2 tablespoons white-wine vinegar, 1 teaspoon olive oil, ¼ teaspoon ground cumin, and ¼ teaspoon salt. Combine ½ cup honeydew melon balls, ¼ sliced avocado, 1 tablespoon sliced scallions, and 1 tablespoon chopped fresh cilantro in large bowl. Toss gently with dressing and sprinkle with 1 teaspoon toasted pepitas.

Jicama

ONCE YOU PEEL OFF THIS TUBER'S PLAIN BROWN WRAPPER you're in for a treat: crisp, juicy, pure-white flesh that has a delightfully sweet flavor and excellent crunch. Almost all jicama is grown in Mexico, where it is traditionally served raw—sometimes accompanied by chili, lime, and salt to accentuate its mild flavor—and is often added to salsa and salads. Jicama can also be cooked; it maintains its excellent crunch and sweetness extremely well in dishes such as stir-fries, soups, and stews.

CHOOSING & STORING

* Choose jicama with smooth, thin, unblemished skins; a slight shine is an indication of freshness.

* Select small or medium tubers; very large ones are often woody and bland and may have a fibrous layer under the skin that will need to be removed during peeling.

* Refrigerate jicama in a paper bag (never in plastic) for up to 2 weeks.

GOOD FOR YOU

Jicama is packed with vitamin C and is a good source of fiber.

TASTE TIPS

* Use a paring knife or vegetable peeler to remove the brown skin from jicama; if there's a tough, fibrous layer under the skin, be sure to remove that as well.

* Grate jicama to add to slaws, salsas, sandwiches, and tacos.

* Slice jicama into matchsticks or batons to use in summer rolls, stir-fries, and salads.

* Diced jicama is excellent steamed or sautéed with other vegetables or added to soups, curries, or stews.

* Serve chunks of raw jicama with tropical fruits like pineapple, mango, and papaya.

* Cut jicama into spears or rounds to serve with dips and dressings, or just sprinkle with lime juice and chili powder for a piquant snack.

Spicy Jicama Chips

Spicy Jicama Chips

Preheat oven to 425°F. Peel ½ small jicama. Cut into paper-thin slices with sharp knife and blot with paper towel. Toss jicama with 1 teaspoon olive oil, ¾ teaspoon chili powder, ½ teaspoon ground cumin, and ¼ teaspoon salt. Spread evenly in baking pan sprayed with nonstick spray. Roast until edges are browned and crisp, about 15 minutes. Serve with ¼ cup fat-free salsa.

Jicama and Green Apple Salad

Whisk together 1 tablespoon apple cider vinegar, 1 teaspoon lime juice, 1 teaspoon olive oil, ½ teaspoon honey, and pinch salt in cup. Combine 1 cup trimmed watercress, 1 cup thin strips of peeled jicama, ½ cup blackberries, and ½ medium Granny Smith apple, cored and cut into thin strips, in medium bowl. Add dressing; toss to coat.

Jicama Waldorf

Combine 1 cup peeled and diced jicama, ½ medium cored and chopped pear, ½ cup seedless grapes, ¼ cup diced celery, 2 tablespoons fat-free mayonnaise, and 2 teaspoons lemon juice in large bowl; toss to mix well.

Kale

IN SEASON **December to February**

NOT ONLY IS THIS STURDY COLD-WEATHER GREEN packed with flavor and character, it also holds the distinction of being one of the most nutrient-dense of all vegetables. Ruffled **curly** kale can be green or purple and has a toothsome texture and a mild, cabbagey flavor. Very dark, slender-leafed **Tuscan** kale (a.k.a. Lacinato kale, dinosaur kale, or cavolo nero) has a particularly rich, earthy flavor and meltingly tender texture when cooked. **Ornamental** kale has lacy leaves that are green at the tips and beautifully tinged with red, white, or violet at the base but is generally too tough for eating.

CHOOSING & STORING

* Select bunches with medium or small to medium leaves and tender looking stems and ribs; very large stems and ribs will have to be discarded, meaning more work and waste.

* Avoid kale with dried-out or yellowed leaves, both a sign of age or poor storage. Leaves with holes in them may mean the plant has been damaged by insects.

* Kale keeps best at low temperatures, so store it in the coldest part of your refrigerator, sealed in a plastic bag, for no more than 2 days.

* Kale is one of the vegetables with the highest pesticide residue, so consider buying organic.

WHAT CHEFS KNOW

* Kale is usually available year-round, but it's sweeter when harvested after the first frost.

* Clean kale by first discarding any yellowed or damaged leaves and then rinsing the bunch very well. Cut off any tough stems from the leaves; if the ribs are thick and tough looking, strip them out with your hands.

* Slice kale leaves very thinly and add raw to salads and slaws.

* Pan-steam kale by combining it in a large skillet with a few tablespoons of water or broth; cover and cook until it reaches the desired tenderness.

* Chop kale and add it to soups, stews, pastas, and casseroles.

* Kale is richly flavored on its own but also pairs well with the strong flavors of soy sauce, chile peppers, onions, garlic, ginger, bacon, vinegar, olives, and feta and Parmesan cheeses.

Kale

Country-Style Kale with Ham

Sauté 2 thinly sliced garlic cloves in 1 teaspoon oil in skillet until fragrant, about 1 minute. Add ¼ cup diced lean low-sodium ham and cook 2 minutes. Add 2 cups trimmed and coarsely chopped kale and ½ cup water; cover and simmer until kale is tender and liquid is almost evaporated, about 15 minutes.

Cider-Braised Kale and Butternut Squash

Place 1 small thinly sliced red onion and 2 minced garlic cloves in saucepan with 1 teaspoon olive oil; cook, stirring, until soft, about 5 minutes. Add ½ cup peeled and cubed butternut squash, 1 cup trimmed and coarsely chopped kale, ¼ cup apple cider, and ¼ cup fat-free low-sodium chicken broth. Cover and simmer until kale is soft and squash is fork-tender, 12–15 minutes.

Kale and Bean Soup

Place 2 chopped scallions, 2 minced garlic cloves, and ½ teaspoon chopped fresh rosemary in saucepan with 1 teaspoon olive oil; cook, stirring, until soft, about 2 minutes. Add 1½ cups fat-free low-sodium chicken broth, 1 cup trimmed and chopped kale leaves, and ½ cup drained cannellini beans; bring to boil. Cover and simmer until kale is very tender, 12–15 minutes.

GOOD FOR YOU

Kale is a nutrition powerhouse. A 1-cup serving provides 350 percent of the vitamin A and 1,300 percent of the vitamin K that you need in a day. It's also an excellent source of a number of powerful antioxidants that may help to protect the body from chronic diseases and promote health.

Country-Style Kale with Ham

Kiwifruit

IN SEASON **Year-round**

SLICE THROUGH A KIWIFRUIT'S UNASSUMING BROWN skin and you'll be rewarded with enticing jewel-like green flesh dotted with black seeds. It's visually stunning, as well as delicious, contrasting creamy, sweet-tart flesh with the pleasant crunch of small seeds. Kiwis are often relegated to garnishing fruit salads and bakery tarts, but they're outstanding as an eat-alone snack or the basis for tropical-tasting salsas, salads, smoothies, and sorbets.

CHOOSING & STORING

Kiwifruit is harvested while still very firm and slowly softens during ripening, increasing in sugar content and flavor.

* Choose firm or soft fruits with unblemished, fuzzy skin. Take a look at the stem end for wrinkling—a sign that the fruit is too ripe.

* Cold retards ripening, allowing you to store firm kiwis in a plastic bag in the refrigerator for several weeks. Let them sit at room temperature for a few days, and they will become soft, juicy, and delicious.

* Speed ripening by placing kiwis in a paper bag with an apple.

WHAT CHEFS KNOW

* Try this easy, neat way to peel a kiwi: Cut a sliver off each end with a paring knife; then make a slit through the skin up the length of the fruit. Slip a metal soupspoon between the skin and the flesh, and work the spoon around the fruit, removing the skin in one neat piece.

* Raw kiwifruit contains the protein-dissolving enzyme actinidin, the same enzyme found in pineapples. For this reason, never use uncooked kiwi in a marinade for meats, don't let it sit for any length of time with dairy, and don't try it with gelatin-based recipes.

GOOD FOR YOU

Kiwifruit is loaded with vitamin C and boasts a number of health-protective antioxidants.

Thai Fruit Salad

Kiwi-Berry Waffle

Toast 1 low-fat frozen waffle and spread with 1 tablespoon fat-free cream cheese. Toss 1 peeled and diced kiwi in small bowl with ½ cup raspberries and ½ teaspoon sugar. Spoon mixture over waffle.

Rainbow Kiwi Salad

Combine 1 chopped red bell pepper, ½ small peeled and cubed mango, 1 large peeled and cubed kiwi, ¼ cup chopped fresh cilantro, and 1 tablespoon rice vinegar in bowl. Sprinkle with 2 teaspoons dried cranberries.

Thai Fruit Salad

Combine 1 large peeled and sliced kiwi, ½ small peeled and cubed papaya, ½ cup pineapple chunks, 2 tablespoons chopped fresh basil leaves, 1 tablespoon lemon juice, and 1 teaspoon peeled and grated fresh ginger in medium bowl; toss until well mixed. Cover and refrigerate until chilled.

LETT

M

MUSHR

O

ORA

Lettuce

IT'S DIFFICULT TO IMAGINE A CULINARY WORLD WITHOUT lettuce. Soft or crunchy, mild or bittersweet, palest yellow to deepest purple—these miraculous greens add beauty, depth, and outstanding nutrition to everyday meals. We think first and foremost of a crisp, raw salad when we think of lettuce, but many varieties are well suited to short cooking in either braises or soups.

CHOOSING & STORING

* Inspect lettuce leaves and heads carefully and reject any that have brown, wilted, or slimy leaves.

* Give lettuce the sniff test: It should smell fresh and grassy, not sour or very earthy.

* Wrap lettuce in a paper towel (this will absorb excess moisture, the enemy of greens' freshness) and then place in a sealed plastic bag in the crisper drawer of your refrigerator. This method should keep it fresh for several days.

* If greens are wilted from summer heat or improper handling, they may revive if soaked in very cold water for a few minutes, spun until bone-dry in a salad spinner, and then wrapped and refrigerated for an hour or two as described above.

* Lettuce is one of the vegetables with the most pesticide residue, so buy organic when possible.

* Rinse lettuce well before using; dirt can hide in the folds of leaves and give you a gritty salad. Additionally, rinsing helps reduce any illness-causing bacteria that may be present and removes some pesticides.

PERFECT SALAD PREP

* Fill a sink or large bowl with cold water and submerge leaves completely. Swish the leaves around gently with your hands and then let the leaves soak for a few minutes; this will allow any sand or grit to sink to the bottom. Scoop leaves up and drain in a colander or salad spinner.

* An alternate method for cleaning greens is to rinse each leaf individually under cold running water and then drain; this is time consuming but may work better if you have sink or space issues.

* Iceberg lettuce is an exception; to clean this dense head you need only remove and discard the outer leaves and then rinse the base. You can also cut around and remove the base, allow water to run through the entire head, and then dry the leaves well.

* A salad spinner is excellent for removing moisture from lettuce. *Continued »*

*L*ettuce

Bibb

Very small, loose heads of soft, loosely curled leaves; buttery, fresh flavor

BEST FOR
Salads, lettuce cups, braising whole heads

GOOD TO KNOW
A member of the butterhead family; smaller than but generally interchangeable with more common Boston

Boston

Small, loose heads of tender, loosely curled leaves; buttery, mineral flavor

BEST FOR
Salads, lettuce wraps, braising whole heads, lining bowls and platters

GOOD TO KNOW
A member of the butterhead family; bruises easily so handle and rinse very gently

Escarole

Broad, frilled leaves with creamy yellow to dark green coloring; fresh, mildly bitter flavor

BEST FOR
Use the lighter, tenderer leaves for salads, or braise or sauté the whole head

GOOD TO KNOW
Actually a member of the endive family

Frisée

Small heads of thin, frilly, very crisp leaves; bittersweet flavor

BEST FOR
Salads, garnish

GOOD TO KNOW
Actually a member of the endive family

Green leaf

Loose heads of tender, rounded, light-green leaves; mild flavor

BEST FOR
Salads, lettuce wraps, lining bowls and platters

GOOD TO KNOW
A top choice for lettuce wraps

Iceberg

Dense, tightly packed heads of extremely crisp light-green leaves; refreshing and very mildly flavored

BEST FOR
Salads, shredding, wedging

GOOD TO KNOW
A high water content makes it the crispest of all lettuces; use for textural contrast

Lollo rosso

Loose heads of ruffled, tender leaves that are light green with brilliant purplish-red edges

BEST FOR
Salads, lettuce wraps, braising whole heads, lining bowls and platters

GOOD TO KNOW
Prized for its attractive color contrast

Mesclun

Mixture of young lettuce and other salad leaves, usually in contrasting colors and shapes

BEST FOR
Salads, garnish

GOOD TO KNOW
Choose carefully; mesclun mixes at their best are fresh, flavorful, and delightful, but they can also be tired, bland and even sour

Radicchio

Small, tightly packed heads of white-veined maroon leaves; lightly bitter flavor

BEST FOR
Salads, braising, grilling, lining bowls and platters

GOOD TO KNOW
Actually a member of the endive family

Red oak

Loose heads of thin, notched, maroon to purple leaves; buttery, mild mineral flavor

BEST FOR
Salads, lining bowls and platters

GOOD TO KNOW
Very attractive when mixed with pale-green leaves

Romaine

Very tall, closely packed heads of crisp, dark green to light green leaves; sweet to bittersweet, mild mineral flavor

BEST FOR
Salads, shredding, braising, grilling

GOOD TO KNOW
Also known as Cos lettuce; crisp enough to substitute for iceberg lettuce in most dishes

Watercress

Tender sprigs of round, jade-green leaves; sprightly, fresh, lightly tangy flavor

BEST FOR
Salads, sandwiches, soups, garnish

GOOD TO KNOW
Actually a member of the cabbage family

Lettuce

If you don't have one, place damp leaves in a single layer on a kitchen towel or double layer of paper towels, roll everything up loosely, and give the roll a few bounces to help pull water out of the leaves. Alternatively, place the leaves in a clean cotton pillowcase, gather the top together in one hand, step outdoors, and windmill your arm, spinning the pillowcase in circles. Centrifugal force will send the moisture flying off the lettuce and out of the pillowcase... goofy, but effective!

* Cut or tear salad greens as close to serving time as possible for best flavor and texture.

* If you do need to refrigerate cut salad greens for more than a few hours, place a paper towel in the bottom of your bowl, add the greens, cover with another paper towel, and seal the top of the bowl with plastic wrap; this will keep most lettuce very fresh for 4 or 5 hours.

* Toss lettuce with dressing only at the last minute for crisp—not limp and soggy—salads.

GOOD FOR YOU

Although nutrient content varies from variety to variety, you can count on most types of lettuce for vitamins K, A, and C; folate and fiber. Choose the darkest varieties for the highest concentrations of nutrients.

Watercress Egg-Drop Soup

Combine 1½ cups fat-free low-sodium chicken broth, 4 ounces sliced shiitake mushrooms, 1 tablespoon peeled and grated fresh ginger, and 1 tablespoon low-sodium soy sauce in saucepan; bring to boil. Reduce heat. Slowly add 2 lightly beaten egg whites, whisking constantly until strands form. Add 1 cup trimmed and chopped watercress, stirring until watercress wilts, about 2 minutes.

Vietnamese Pork and Lettuce Cups

Sauté 1 tablespoon minced shallot and 1 teaspoon peeled and grated fresh ginger in 1 teaspoon canola oil in skillet 1 minute. Add ¼ pound lean ground pork and cook, breaking up with spoon, until browned, about 5 minutes. Stir in 1 teaspoon low-sodium soy sauce. Let cool slightly. Divide pork mixture evenly between 2 large Boston lettuce leaves. Top each with 2 tablespoons shredded carrot and 1 tablespoon thinly sliced scallions.

BLT Salad

Toss 2 cups chopped romaine lettuce, ½ cup halved cherry tomatoes, ¼ cubed peeled avocado, and 1 tablespoon chopped red onion in bowl. Drizzle with 2 tablespoons fat-free blue cheese dressing and sprinkle with 1 slice crumbled crisply cooked turkey bacon.

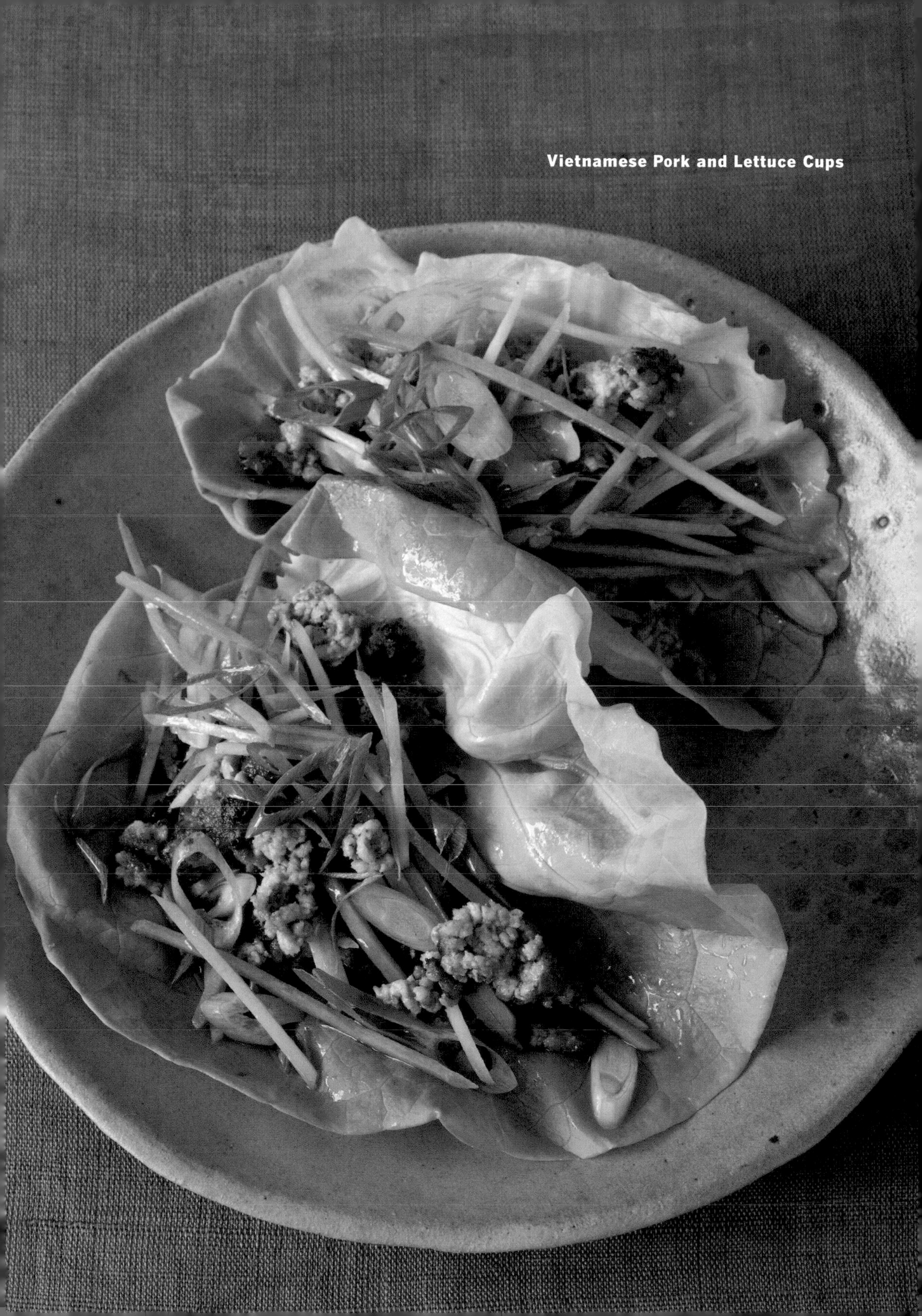
Vietnamese Pork and Lettuce Cups

Mangos

IN SEASON **June to August**

MANGOS ARE CULTIVATED IN JUST ABOUT EVERY WARM climate across the globe and are one of the world's favorite fruits. Their popularity lags a bit here in the United States, but with rich, lusciously tropical flesh and a host of impressive health benefits they're gaining fans fast. Mango varieties vary widely in size, color, flavor, and texture but are only sometimes, not always, sold by name. Some common varieties in our markets are large **Tommy Atkins,** supersweet **Kietts,** and buttery **Kents.**

CHOOSING & STORING

* Skin color varies from variety to variety, so don't rely on it as a predictor of ripeness unless you're familiar with the type.

* Press mangos gently at the stem end; a ripe mango should give slightly and smell sweet and tropical.

* Firm mangos will ripen slowly at room temperature, although those harvested when immature and rock hard may never ripen properly.

* As they ripen, keep mangos away from sunlight or very warm temperatures as these may adversely affect their flavor.

* Speed ripening by storing mangos in a bag with an apple.

* Wrinkled skin, black splotches, and a fermented aroma are signs of overripe fruit.

* Freeze mangos by peeling and dicing the flesh and placing it in zip-close freezer bags or airtight containers.

WHAT CHEFS KNOW

* The majority of a mango's flesh can be sliced away from the large, central pit in two "cheeks." You can slice the sides of the mango again to yield two smaller strips of flesh.

* Once you have removed the cheeks, score deep lengthwise and cross-wise cuts into them, cutting almost to the skin; you should have a checkerboard of small squares. Push gently on the skin to turn the fruit slightly inside out, then release the cubes of flesh with a paring knife or teaspoon. Alternatively, slice the cheeks into strips and then use a paring knife to cut away the skin.

* Use diced mango in salads, chutneys, and salsas.

* Add sliced mango to sandwiches and wraps.

* Break out the blender and some fat-free plain yogurt and ice cubes and you're a few pulses away from a delicious mango lassi.

Mangos

Caribbean Glazed Mango

Sauté 1 teaspoon finely chopped lemongrass in 1 teaspoon canola oil in skillet until fragrant, about 1 minute. Add ½ small peeled and sliced mango and 1 large sliced star fruit. Cook until fruit just begins to soften, about 2 minutes. Sprinkle with 1 teaspoon packed brown sugar and cook until fruit is glazed, 1–2 minutes longer.

Mango-Tofu Curry

Sauté ½ chopped red bell pepper in skillet sprayed with nonstick spray until crisp-tender, 3–4 minutes. Add ¼ cup fat-free low-sodium chicken broth, ¼ teaspoon Thai red curry paste, and pinch salt; bring to boil. Stir in ½ small peeled and cubed mango, ¼ cup firm cubed tofu, and 1 tablespoon chopped fresh basil. Cook until heated through, about 2 minutes longer.

Cool Mango Couscous

Toss ½ cup cooked and cooled whole wheat couscous with ½ cup peeled and diced mango, 2 chopped pitted prunes, 1 tablespoon finely chopped scallion, 1 tablespoon orange juice, and a pinch each salt and pepper.

GOOD FOR YOU

Mangos are bursting with vitamins and minerals and are one of the best sources of the antioxidants beta-carotene and lycopene. A cup of sliced mango provides 36 percent of the vitamin A and nearly all of the vitamin C that you need in a day. All that, and an impressive 3 g of fiber too.

Caribbean Glazed Mango

Mushrooms

VENTURE BEYOND THE COMMON WHITE BUTTON mushroom and you'll enter an intriguing and rewarding world of hundreds of delicious varieties. Adding to mushrooms' mystery is the fact that they aren't really vegetables at all, but rather fungi that grow and reproduce without the benefit of roots, leaves, seeds, or flowers. Until recently, most mushroom varieties resisted cultivation, making them local specialties available only to foragers or restaurateurs willing to pay top dollar. New growing techniques have expanded the number of varieties now commercially available, and even those commonly labeled "wild" at your market were probably harvested by specialty growers.

CHOOSING & STORING

Characteristics vary widely from variety to variety, but here are some general tips:

* Mushrooms should be springy and somewhat dense in texture; avoid any that are limp, spongy, or dried out.

* Never buy mushrooms that have slimy spots on them, a sign of water damage.

* Caps should be smooth and free of cracks, breaks, or nibble marks, and stems should be free of holes (a sign of insect damage in wild mushrooms).

* Mushrooms should have a pleasantly earthy aroma; mushrooms that smell musty or sour will probably taste that way.

* Refrigerate mushrooms in the box they came in, or wrap them in a paper bag or a double thickness of paper towels. They should be stored as far away from moisture as possible, so opt to leave them on a shelf rather than in a vegetable drawer.

CLEANING MUSHROOMS

* Use a soft brush or a damp paper towel to remove any loose dirt from mushroom caps and stems.

* Avoid rinsing mushrooms unless they are very gritty and dirty, and never soak them: mushrooms absorb water quickly, becoming soggy and unappealing, so keep their contact with water minimal and blot them dry with paper towels immediately.

* Trim off woody stems, tough bases, or any discolored areas with a paring knife; you can save the scraps to flavor soups or stocks.

* Splitting mushroom varieties with hollow centers (like morels) will allow you to remove dirt or insects that may be hiding there.

Mushrooms

Black trumpet

Dark brown to black, with a delicate trumpet shape; slightly chewy with deep, earthy flavor

BEST FOR
Sautéing, steaming, soups

GOOD TO KNOW
Strong flavor and dramatic appearance make them a favorite in wild mushroom mixes

Bluefoot

Beige caps and stems with hints of lavender; meaty and lightly earthy

BEST FOR
Sautéing, roasting, soups

GOOD TO KNOW
Also known as blewitts

Chanterelle

Bright yellow to orange with a frilled, trumpet-like shape; rich, buttery, and earthy flavor with an aroma like ripe apricots

BEST FOR
Sautéing, roasting, soups

GOOD TO KNOW
A favorite for its distinctive coloring and deep flavor

Cremini

Dark brown, squat, and meaty; smoky, lightly nutty in flavor

BEST FOR
Eating raw, sautéing, steaming, roasting, grilling, soups

GOOD TO KNOW
Young portobello mushroom, sometimes called "baby bella"; a flavorful all-purpose mushroom

Enoki

Small ivory caps with very long, slender stems; sweet and earthy with pronounced crunch

BEST FOR
Eating raw, sautéing, steaming, soups

GOOD TO KNOW
Preserve enokis' distinctive crisp texture by eating them raw or with very brief cooking

Hen of the Wood

Large brown to beige, leafy clusters; very meaty; rich, spicy flavor

BEST FOR
Sautéing, roasting

GOOD TO KNOW
Also known as maitake, these tree mushrooms are superb for roasting

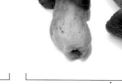

Morel

Thick, tube-like stems with a honeycombed cap; very intense smoky, nutty, earthy flavor

BEST FOR
Sautéing, roasting, soups

GOOD TO KNOW
Prized for its strong flavor and sponge-like ability to absorb other flavors

Oyster

Brown to gray to yellow with soft, velvety stems and caps; sweet, delicate flavor

BEST FOR
Sautéing, steaming, roasting, soups

GOOD TO KNOW
Excellent for stir-fries and quick sautés

Porcini

Bulbous beige or ivory stems topped with golden-brown caps; rich, smoky flavor and deep, woodsy aroma

BEST FOR
Sautéing, roasting, soups

GOOD TO KNOW
Dried porcini are readily available and flavorful but lack the creamy, meaty texture prized in the fresh mushrooms

Portobello

Huge brown caps with brown to black gills; deep earthy, lightly sweet and oaky flavor

BEST FOR
Sautéing, roasting, grilling

GOOD TO KNOW
These oversized caps are excellent for stuffing or grilling and slicing

Shiitake

Very tough stems topped with dark-brown, flexible caps; rich, meaty flavor and woodsy aroma

BEST FOR
Sautéing, steaming, roasting, grilling, soups

GOOD TO KNOW
Although edible, the stems are so fibrous that they are usually used only to flavor stocks or sauces

White

Firm, thick white caps and squat stems; very mild woodsy flavor

BEST FOR
Eating raw, sautéing, roasting, grilling, soups

GOOD TO KNOW
Good all-purpose mushroom for everything from salads to kebabs to stuffing

Mushrooms

* Only a few mushroom varieties (including white mushrooms, cremini, and enokis) are suitable for eating raw; others (like portobello and oyster mushrooms) will have an overly musty flavor or tough texture, and morels can cause gastric upset if eaten raw.

* Sautéing is one of the best ways to concentrate the flavor of mushrooms and enjoy them in everything from omelets to salads to soups to pastas. For best results, use medium-high heat, don't overcrowd the pan, and stir frequently until the mushrooms are tender and their liquid has evaporated.

* Roasting is also a great cooking option: Use a hot oven (400°F–425°F) and roast the mushrooms until they are browned and tender, stirring once or twice during cooking.

* Mushrooms are superb grilled. Larger varieties such as portobellos can be grilled like burgers, and smaller, firm mushrooms like creminis and white mushrooms cook excellently on metal skewers.

GOOD FOR YOU

Traditional Chinese medicine has touted the health benefits of mushrooms for centuries, and modern science has given these beliefs some validation. Preliminary research suggests that a unique blend of vitamins, minerals, and antioxidants in mushrooms may help protect our cells from a number of cancers, including breast cancer and colon cancer.

Cheesy Mushroom Pizzette

Cook 2 thinly sliced cremini mushrooms and 1 sliced shallot in skillet sprayed with nonstick spray until tender, about 5 minutes. Spread 1 tablespoon fat-free ricotta cheese on ½ toasted whole wheat English muffin. Top with 1 tomato slice. Spoon mushrooms over top, sprinkle with 2 tablespoons fat-free mozzarella, and broil until cheese is bubbly.

Roasted Shiitake Mushrooms with Orange and Rosemary

Preheat oven to 425°F. Place ½ pound whole stemmed shiitake mushrooms on baking pan; lightly spray with nonstick spray and toss with 1 minced garlic clove. Roast until tender, about 10 minutes. Toss in bowl with ½ small sectioned orange, 1 teaspoon chopped fresh rosemary, 1 teaspoon olive oil, and pinch salt.

Mushroom, Potato, and Spinach Soup

Cook 1 cup sliced mushrooms and 2 tablespoons chopped scallions in 1 teaspoon olive oil until tender, about 5 minutes. Add 1½ cups fat-free low-sodium chicken broth and 1 small cubed red potato; cover and simmer until potato is tender, 12–15 minutes. Transfer ½ cup soup to blender and puree; return to saucepan. Stir in 2 cups baby spinach and cook until spinach is wilted, 1–2 minutes.

Cheesy Mushroom Pizzette

Onions

IN SEASON Year-round

WHO COULD IMAGINE COOKING WITHOUT ONIONS? THIS venerable vegetable has a long, storied history stretching back so far that even experts disagree on its culinary origins. Today onions find their way into almost every savory dish in almost every land, from soups and stews to curries and stir-fries. Onions are loosely classified as either dry, or "storage," onions, with papery brown, yellow, or red skins; or fresh, young "green onions," including scallions, leeks, and spring onions. Both share the *Allium* genus's bold combination of sweetness and pungency.

CHOOSING & STORING

* Look for onions with tight, dry, papery skins; shiny onions stripped of their fragile skins will not keep well. Avoid onions with green sprouts, a sign of age or incorrect storage.

* Onions store best in a basket kept in a cool, dark place; do not refrigerate onions.

* If buying green onions (scallions, spring onions, or leeks), look for glossy white bulbs and fresh, sprightly green tops.

* Store green onions in a sealed plastic bag in the coldest part of the refrigerator for up to a week.

GOOD FOR YOU

Onions have nutritionists talking, although the buzz isn't about their vitamin content. They do contain modest amounts of vitamin C, plus a good dose of fiber. But it's their combination of flavonoids and powerful sulfur-containing compounds that have led researchers to believe they might have cardiovascular and anti-cancer benefits. Stay tuned.

WHAT CHEFS KNOW

* The skins of baby onions will slip off most easily if you pour boiling water over them and let them soak 5 minutes. Drain and cool under cold running water. Cut a sliver from the root end of each and the skin should slip off without taking layers of the onion with it.

* Choose sweet onion varieties like Vidalia, Walla Walla, or Maui for serving raw in salads, sandwiches, tacos, and on burgers. You can also tame more pungent varieties by slicing them and soaking them in ice water for 30 minutes, draining them, and blotting them dry.

* Onion prices have risen dramatically in the past few years, making cooks hesitant to waste even a scrap. You can store onion skins and ends and the trimmings from scallions and leeks in a zip-close bag in the freezer and use them next time you make a stock or broth.

Onions

Baby

Very small, with mild to moderate bite and earthy flavor

BEST FOR
Roasting, braising, pickling

GOOD TO KNOW
Also known as pickling or boiling onions; can be any variety of early-harvested, immature onion

Cipollini

Small, disc-shaped, with rich, sweet, earthy flavor and mild bite

BEST FOR
Roasting, braising, pickling

GOOD TO KNOW
Prized for their complex flavor and unusual button-like shape

Leek

Thick white stalk and broad dark-green leaves with a sweet, fresh, and mild onion flavor

BEST FOR
Roasting, braising, soups

GOOD TO KNOW
Fibrous when raw but meltingly tender with cooking

Maui

Large, crisp, very sweet and mild

BEST FOR
Slicing, salads, grilling

GOOD TO KNOW
In season April to July

Pearl

Very small, very mild onion about the size of a large marble

BEST FOR
Roasting, braising, pickling, garnishing

GOOD TO KNOW
Peeling these minis can be time consuming, making them a popular onion to buy frozen and pan ready

Red

Medium to large, deep purple or magenta, and very crisp with mild to moderate bite

BEST FOR
Slicing, salads, grilling, roasting

GOOD TO KNOW
A very versatile onion: an excellent flavor and color addition to salads, plus firm texture and good flavor balance for cooking

Scallion

Slender white base and long green leaves with mild onion flavor

BEST FOR
Slicing, salads, stir-fries, garnish, grilling, soups

GOOD TO KNOW
Also known as green onions

Spanish

Large, fairly mild and juicy

BEST FOR
Salads, sautéing, caramelizing, soups, grilling, roasting

GOOD TO KNOW
A good choice for both eating raw and cooking

Spring

Small to medium snow white onions with abundant greenery on top; fresh tasting with balanced sweet-pungent flavor

BEST FOR
Slicing, salads, roasting, braising, soups

GOOD TO KNOW
Use the green tops as well as the white bulbs

Texas sweet

Large, crisp, very sweet

BEST FOR
Slicing, salads, grilling, baking

GOOD TO KNOW
In season March to April

Vidalia

Large, crisp, juicy, very sweet and mild

BEST FOR
Slicing, salads, grilling

GOOD TO KNOW
In season April to June

Walla Walla

Large, crisp, very sweet and mild

BEST FOR
Slicing, salads, grilling

GOOD TO KNOW
In season June to August

White

Tangy, pungent and very crisp

BEST FOR
Sautéing, roasting, baking

GOOD TO KNOW
A good all-purpose cooking onion

Yellow

Juicy, pungent

BEST FOR
Sautéing, roasting, baking

GOOD TO KNOW
A good all-purpose cooking onion

Onions

BRINGING TEARS TO OUR EYES

Onions have volatile sulfur compounds that are released into the air when their cell walls are cut. These compounds reduce some cooks to tears, while others can cut onion after onion with barely a sniff. Try these tricks if you're in the former category:

* Refrigerate onions for 30 minutes before cutting to help minimize the release of sulfur.

* Make sure your knife is very sharp—a honed blade will cut through the cell walls neatly, releasing less sulfur.

* Turn on your kitchen exhaust fan and chop on a cutting board set directly underneath the fan.

* Wear a pair of safety goggles while you chop.

* Good news for contact lens wearers: Contacts actually provide a level of protection against onion fumes and their irritation.

Red Onion and Chickpea Salad

Combine ½ cup drained canned chickpeas with ¼ small thinly sliced red onion, ¼ cup diced cucumber, 2 teaspoons chopped fresh parsley, 1 tablespoon lemon juice, 1 teaspoon olive oil, and pinch each salt and pepper.

Crunchy Onion Rings

Preheat oven to 450°F. Cut ½ large onion into ½-inch rounds and separate into 8 rings. Place 1 tablespoon all-purpose flour in zip-close bag. Add rings and shake to coat. Whisk 2 large egg whites and ½ teaspoon hot sauce in bowl. Place 4 teaspoons cornflake crumbs on plate. Dip rings, one at a time, in egg white mixture; then coat with crumbs. Place on small baking sheet and lightly spray with nonstick spray. Bake until golden, about 20 minutes.

Caramelized Sweet Onion Quesadilla

Sauté 1 small thinly sliced Vidalia onion, ½ teaspoon thyme, and pinch salt in 1 teaspoon olive oil in skillet until very tender, about 10 minutes. Place 1 small fat-free tortilla on work surface; spoon onion mixture evenly over bottom half of tortilla. Top with 1 (1-ounce) slice lean ham. Sprinkle with 2 tablespoons shredded fat-free Cheddar cheese. Fold top half of tortilla over filling, pressing down lightly. Wipe skillet clean. Spray with nonstick spray and heat over medium-high heat. Add quesadilla and cook until browned and crisp, 2–3 minutes per side.

Crunchy Onion Rings

Oranges

IN SEASON November to March

NOTHING BEATS THE CHEERY FLAVOR AND BRIGHT aroma of a really good orange. Better yet, they just happen to come into their peak during the cooler months, when we most appreciate their sunny taste and immunity-boosting vitamin C. Sweet, juicy, thick-skinned **navel** oranges are the most popular for peeling and eating. **Valencias** are classic juice oranges with thinner skin, some seeds, and very flavorful flesh. Red-tinged **blood** oranges have distinctive maroon to dark purple flesh that is sweet and spicy. Easy-to-peel **Cara Cara** oranges boast juicy flesh with a pinkish hue.

CHOOSING & STORING

One of life's small disappointments is peeling an orange in anticipation of a sweet, juicy treat and instead finding a dried, tasteless mass. Judging from the exterior alone can be difficult, but these tips and storage suggestions can help.

* Lift oranges before you buy them; heaviness for their size is usually a sign of juiciness.

* Don't rely on skin color alone; oranges are sometimes dyed to look more vibrant. Keep in mind that some greening on the skin will not affect quality, nor will rough brown patches known as russeting.

* Look for thicker skins on fruit that you want to peel, thinner skins on fruit you want to cut or juice.

* Store oranges for several days at room temperature, but refrigerate them to keep them fresh for a week or more.

* Even if you're not planning to use the zest immediately, you can remove it before you peel an orange and freeze it. Use a zester or Microplane, wrap the zest securely in plastic wrap, and freeze it up to 3 months.

WHAT CHEFS KNOW

* To remove orange flesh in neat segments, first cut thin slices from both the top and bottom of a fruit. Set it on a cutting board and cut down along the curve of the fruit, removing all the peel and pith and cutting all the way to flesh. Now hold the whole skinless fruit over a bowl and cut along the membranes to release each segment, letting the segments and any juice drop into the bowl. Pick out and discard any seeds.

* Want an easier method for preparing oranges for salads or desserts? Use a small serrated knife to remove the peel and white pith in a spiral. Halve the peeled orange lengthwise, then slice each half into thin half moons and remove any seeds.

* Oranges go exceptionally well with the flavors of spinach, winter greens, fennel, garlic, shallots, chiles, fresh herbs, olives, seafood, poultry, chocolate, cinnamon, coconut, red wine, and almonds.

Oranges

Orange-Spinach Salad with Curry Vinaigrette

Combine 2 cups baby spinach, 1 medium peeled and sectioned orange, and ½ chopped yellow bell pepper in bowl. Whisk together 1 tablespoon apple cider vinegar, 1 teaspoon curry powder, 1 teaspoon olive oil, and ½ teaspoon salt in small bowl. Drizzle dressing over salad, tossing to coat.

Orange-Roasted Root Vegetables

Preheat oven to 450°F. Cut 1 unpeeled orange into 6 wedges. Toss in bowl with 1 medium peeled and cubed parsnip, 1 small cubed carrot, 1 teaspoon chopped fresh thyme, 1 teaspoon olive oil, and pinch each salt and pepper. Place in a single layer in roasting pan. Roast until tender and browned, about 20 minutes.

Orange-Rosemary Grilled Salmon

Combine 1 teaspoon chopped fresh rosemary, 2 teaspoons orange juice, and ¼ teaspoon salt in small bowl. Add 1 (4-ounce) salmon fillet and toss to coat. Cut 1 unpeeled orange crosswise into ½-inch rounds; sprinkle with 1 teaspoon chopped fresh rosemary. Grill salmon and orange slices in grill pan sprayed with nonstick spray until salmon is cooked through and oranges are tender and well marked, 6–8 minutes.

GOOD FOR YOU

In addition to an abundance of vitamin C, a medium orange contains 4 g of fiber, most of it the soluble fiber pectin, which helps eliminate excess cholesterol from the body. Oranges also contain heart-healthy potassium and magnesium and a variety of antioxidants.

Orange-Rosemary Grilled Salmon

PEA

NECTA

PINEA

PLU

POMEGR

POT

Peaches & Nectarines

IN SEASON June to September

SUMMER'S GLORIOUS PEACHES AND NECTARINES ARE SO similar in flavor and appearance that it's hardly surprising they're separated by a single gene (it's responsible for the fuzziness of peaches). Both fruits are commonly classified as either **white** or **yellow** depending on the color of their flesh; some connoisseurs claim that the less common white fruit has a finer flavor.

CHOOSING & STORING

* Opt for locally grown peaches and nectarines for best flavor and texture: They're more likely to have been ripened on the tree and less likely to have been bruised or otherwise mishandled in transport.

* Choose plump fruit with unblemished skin and absolutely no signs of bruising.

* Fruit harvested at proper ripeness will give just a little when pressed with your fingertip.

* Follow your nose! Flavorful peaches and nectarines should have a distinctly sweet, floral aroma.

* Leave peaches and nectarines at room temperature to soften, but be aware that they will not increase in sugar content or improve in flavor.

* Refrigerate soft fruit for a day or two.

* Peaches and nectarines are two of the fruits with the most pesticide residue, so always rinse them well; better yet, buy organic when you can.

TASTE TIPS

* Slice or dice peaches and nectarines and add to savory salads.

* Dice peaches and nectarines and use as the base for a summery salsa.

* Cooking deepens and sweetens the flavor of peaches and nectarines, so turn on the stove or spark up the grill if you've got some fruit with less-than-outstanding flavor.

* Try grilling peach halves or cutting them into thick wedges and threading them on kebabs with chicken, pork, or tofu.

* Pair peaches and nectarines with herbs and spices, especially thyme, lavender, mint, ginger, cinnamon, and black pepper. Flavorings like vanilla, soy sauce, balsamic vinegar, honey, brown sugar, and wine also work well with the fruit. Other ingredients that harmonize with them include almonds, pecans, cherries, blueberries, ham, pork, mild cheeses, and smoked foods.

Peaches & Nectarines

PITTING & PEELING 101

* Freestone peaches and nectarines are bred with a loose pit that is easily removed: simply cut through the fruit to the pit, turn the fruit to cut all the way around the pit, and then use your hands to twist the halves in opposite directions.

* Clingstone pits are more tenaciously fused to the fruits' flesh. You'll need to cut completely around the pit to remove the flesh.

* Smooth-skinned nectarines usually don't need to be peeled if eaten raw; if the fuzz on peaches bothers you, gently scrub them under cold running water to remove some of it.

* Fruit that will be cooked will sometimes need to be peeled first. Score an X on the bottom of each, drop into boiling water for 15 seconds, then transfer to a bowl of cold water to cool. You should be able to remove the skin with your fingers.

GOOD FOR YOU

Peaches and nectarines are packed with potassium and vitamins A and C. They also contain a host of antioxidants, including flavonoids, carotenes, lycopene, and lutein, which may help in preventing a number of illnesses, including cancer and heart disease.

Microwave Peach Crisp

Chop 1 medium peach and toss with 1 teaspoon lemon juice in small microwavable dish. Combine 1 tablespoon old-fashioned rolled oats, 1 teaspoon packed brown sugar, 1 teaspoon unsalted butter, and ¼ teaspoon ground cinnamon in cup; sprinkle evenly over peaches. Microwave on High until peaches are soft and topping is set, 3–4 minutes.

Nectarine and Black Bean Salsa

Dice 1 medium nectarine and toss with ¼ cup drained black beans, 1 chopped scallion, 1 tablespoon chopped fresh cilantro, 2 tablespoons lime juice, 1 teaspoon olive oil, ½ seeded minced jalapeño pepper, and ¼ teaspoon salt.

Glazed Peach and Pork Kebabs

Cut 1 small peach into 6 wedges and thread on 4 small skewers with ¼ pound cubed boneless pork loin and ½ red bell pepper cut into 1-inch pieces. Brush kebabs with 1 tablespoon apricot fruit spread and sprinkle with ¼ teaspoon salt. Place kebabs on grill pan or broiler rack lightly sprayed with nonstick spray and cook, turning once, until pork is no longer pink in center, 8–10 minutes.

Glazed Peach and Pork Kebabs

Pears

IN SEASON August to December

BITE INTO A TRULY RIPE PEAR AND IT'S HARD NOT TO smile as you reach for a few extra napkins. At their best, pears are sublimely sweet, with rich, buttery flesh that fairly bursts with juice. And talk about versatile: They're just as delicious incorporated into savory dishes as sweet ones and cook up beautifully whether baked, broiled, poached, or grilled.

CHOOSING & STORING

Commercially grown pears have made a unique path to our tables. Harvested while still hard, they are "cured" in cold storage for several weeks and then brought to room temperature to complete ripening, a process that usually begins while the fruit is on your market's shelves and ends in your fruit bowl. Asian pears are an exception; this variety is generally fully ripened and should be eaten within a few days.

* Select pears that are free of soft spots, nicks, or cuts.

* Skin color varies from variety to variety, so don't use it as a gauge of quality or ripeness unless you are familiar with the type.

* Unripe pears should be left at room temperature to ripen, a process that usually takes 2 to 6 days. Place them in a bag with an apple to speed ripening.

* Pears are ripe when they give just a little when pressed at the neck end and have a sweet, floral aroma when sniffed. Slightly underripe fruit will hold its shape better during cooking.

TASTE TIPS

* Enjoy pears at breakfast in cereal, in omelets, over yogurt, or diced as a topping for pancakes or waffles.

* Make a quick pear compote by stewing diced pears (peeled or unpeeled) in a little bit of water or apple juice until soft. It's excellent with roast meats or as a dessert sauce.

* Mix pears with more strongly flavored fruits like cranberries, blueberries, or peaches. Or combine with rhubarb for exceptional pies and cobblers.

* Poached pears are a popular dessert, and poaching is a particularly good way to enjoy pears that are not quite ripe enough to eat raw. Wine or fruit juice are popular poaching liquids; classic flavorings include cloves, cinnamon sticks, star anise, orange peel, and rosemary.
Continued »

Pears

Anjou

Rounded and green, sometimes with a reddish blush; juicy, creamy, and very sweet

BEST FOR
Eating raw, slicing, baking

GOOD TO KNOW
Late-season pear with excellent flavor, sometimes known as the "Christmas pear"

Asian

Round; yellow or russet skin; very crisp, mildly flavored, honey-sweet flesh with a lightly gritty texture

BEST FOR
Eating raw, slicing

GOOD TO KNOW
A high water content makes this pear a very refreshing snack

Bartlett

Bell-shaped, with skin that turns from green to yellow when ripe; mild, juicy flesh with a smooth texture

BEST FOR
Eating raw, slicing

GOOD TO KNOW
Also known as Williams

Bosc

Long, curved neck and russet gold skin; spicy, crunchy, and very firm

BEST FOR
Baking, poaching, broiling

GOOD TO KNOW
Good flavor and ability to keep its shape during cooking make it a top choice for poaching and broiling

Comice

Large and rounded with yellow-green skin; honey-sweet, creamy flesh with intense floral flavor and aroma

BEST FOR
Eating raw, slicing

GOOD TO KNOW
One of the best choices for serving with cheese

Forelle

Small, with deep yellow skin blushing to scarlet; very sweet, firm flesh

BEST FOR
Eating raw, slicing, baking, poaching, broiling

GOOD TO KNOW
Prized for their adorable size and bright color; firm flesh makes them good for cooking, although their small stature can make peeling and coring time-consuming

French butter

Bell-shaped, with golden russet skin; creamy, juicy flesh with sweet, spicy, caramel-like flavor

BEST FOR
Eating raw, slicing, broiling

GOOD TO KNOW
Less commonly available, but worth seeking out for its superb rich flavor and smooth texture

Red Anjou

Rounded and deep red; juicy, creamy, and very sweet

BEST FOR
Eating raw, slicing, baking

GOOD TO KNOW
A beautiful pear for salads and cheese plates; leave them unpeeled to enjoy their vivid color

Red Bartlett

Bell-shaped, with skin that turns from brick to bright red when ripe; mild, juicy flesh with a smooth texture

BEST FOR
Eating raw, slicing

GOOD TO KNOW
A beautiful pear for salads and cheese plates; leave them unpeeled to enjoy their vivid color

Seckel

Small, with yellow-green flesh speckled with red; very crisp, sweet, and tangy

BEST FOR
Slicing, baking, broiling

GOOD TO KNOW
One of the smallest pear varieties, lovely for garnishing platters and cheese plates and popular in centerpieces

Pears

* Asian pears should always be eaten raw, as they are generally too mild and have too high a water content to hold up to cooking; they're excellent in salads and on sandwiches.

* Pears are an outstanding complement to cheeses. Try them on a cheese plate, in salads, or as a dessert course topped with a soft cheese like goat cheese, ricotta, or mascarpone.

* After cutting, pears will darken when exposed to oxygen for several hours; although this will not affect flavor, you can keep them more attractive by brushing cut surfaces with lemon juice or orange juice or by tossing them with an acidic dressing.

GOOD FOR YOU

Not only do pears have an impressive 5 g of heart-healthy fiber, they also contain epicatechin, a phytochemical that preliminary research suggests may help prevent heart disease and some types of cancer.

Spiced Pear Frappé

Place ½ cup pear nectar in blender with ½ small cored and chopped Bartlett pear, ¼ cup low-fat buttermilk, 3 ice cubes, and ½ teaspoon almond extract; blend until smooth. Pour into glass and sprinkle with pinch ground cinnamon.

Open-Face Ham and Pear Grilled Cheese

Spread 1 slice toasted whole wheat bread with 1 teaspoon honey mustard. Top with 1 slice smoked deli ham, and 1 slice (¾-ounce) lite Jarlsberg cheese. Broil until cheese is melted. Top with ¼ cored and thinly sliced red pear.

Pear and Sweet Potato Mash

Core, peel, and chop 1 small pear. Combine with ½ cup peeled and cubed sweet potato and 1 tablespoon peeled and grated fresh ginger in saucepan. Add ¼ cup fat-free reduced-sodium chicken broth; cover and simmer until pear and potato are very tender, about 15 minutes. Mash and stir in 1 teaspoon butter, ⅛ teaspoon freshly grated nutmeg, and pinch salt.

Open-Face Ham and
Pear Grilled Cheese

Pineapple

IN SEASON **Year-round**

PINEAPPLE IS SO GOOD RAW THAT MANY COOKS DON'T think about incorporating it into everyday cooking and baking, which is a shame: It's superb baked, broiled, grilled, stir-fried, and tossed into soups and salads. Just remember that fresh pineapple contains bromelain, an enzyme that breaks down protein, so don't add it to most dishes until just before serving and avoid using it with gelatin.

CHOOSING & STORING

Contrary to popular belief, pineapples do not ripen after harvest, so spend a few moments to make sure the one you select is ready for eating.

* Give pineapples a sniff: They should have a rich, sweet, tropical aroma that will be strongest at the fruit's base.

* Look at the skin; it should be deeply colored and bright, although the hue (yellow, yellow-green, brown, or red) varies from variety to variety. It should give slightly when firmly pressed with your fingertip.

* Pineapple leaves should be crisp and green, with no yellowing or browning at the tips. A center leaf should come out with a gentle tug if the fruit is ripe.

* Slightly underripe pineapples can be left at room temperature for a few days to soften, but remember that they will not increase in sugar content.

* Soft, ripe pineapples can be refrigerated for 3 to 4 days.

PEELING & PARING 101

* Cut off the top and bottom of the pineapple. Set it on a cutting board and cut down to remove all the skin; use a paring knife to remove any small brown "eyes" set deeply into the flesh.

* For rings, cut the peeled pineapple into slices and remove the core of each with a small round cookie cutter.

* For chunks, cut the peeled pineapple lengthwise into quarters and then slice the core out of each quarter.

* Many produce departments sell freshly peeled and cored pineapples, or you can try out any of a number of easy and effective peeling and coring gadgets.

GOOD FOR YOU

One cup of pineapple chunks provides a day's worth of vitamin C.

Wheat Berry Salad with Currants and Pineapple

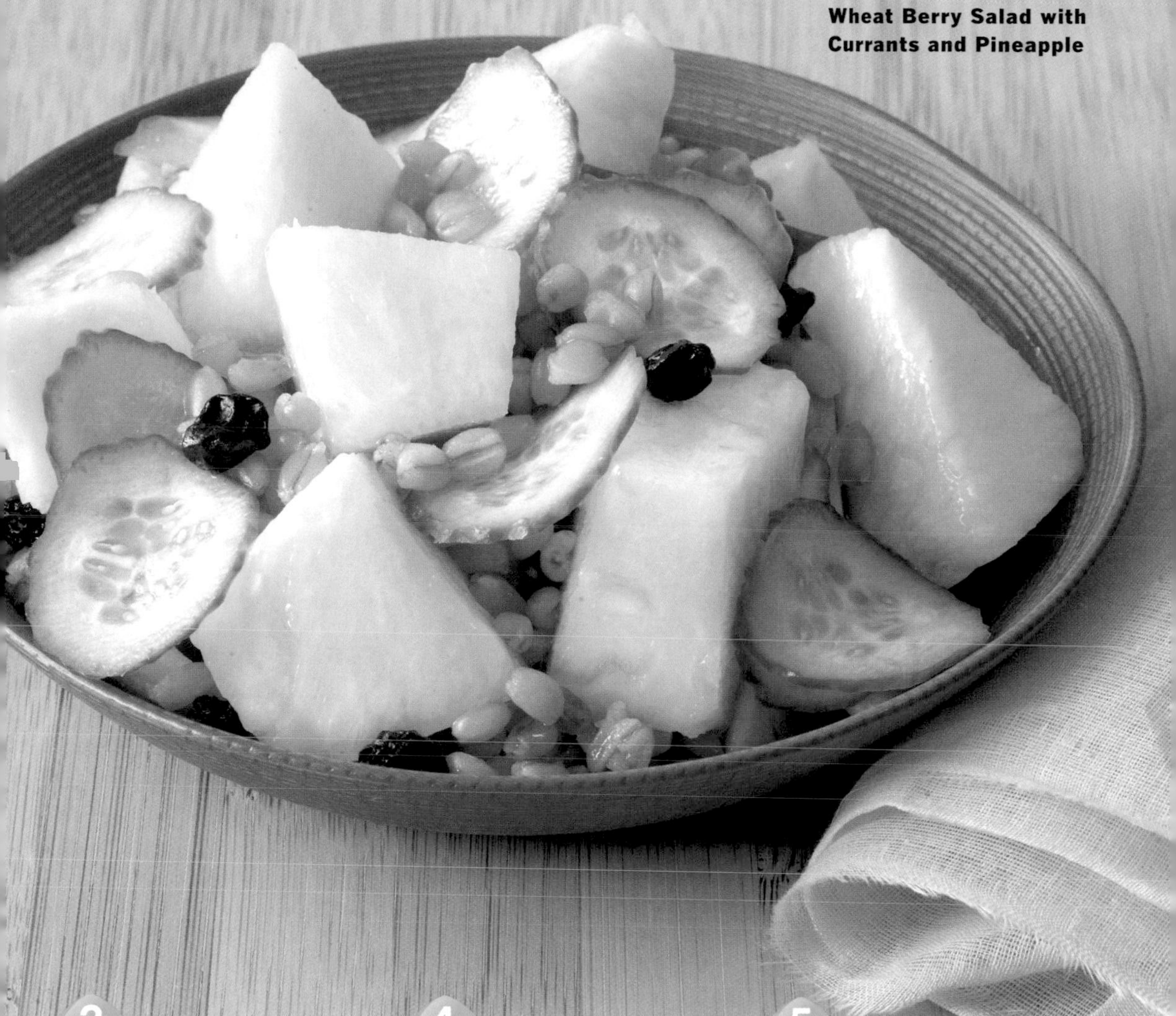

2 PointsPlus® value

Pina Colada Sorbet

Toss ½ cup diced pineapple with 1 teaspoon grated lemon zest. Scoop ¼ cup lemon sorbet into bowl; top with diced pineapple.

4 PointsPlus® value

Wheat Berry Salad with Currants and Pineapple

Whisk together 1 tablespoon minced shallot, 1 tablespoon rice vinegar, 1 teaspoon olive oil, and ¼ teaspoon salt in bowl. Stir in ½ cup cubed pineapple, ¼ cup cooked wheat berries, ¼ cup sliced cucumber, and 1 teaspoon dried currants.

5 PointsPlus® value

Pineapple-Kiwi Mojito Salad

Toss 1 cup diced pineapple, 1 peeled and diced kiwifruit, 2 tablespoons chopped fresh mint, 2 tablespoons lime juice, and 1 teaspoon packed brown sugar in bowl. Cover and refrigerate until chilled.

Plums

IN SEASON **June to September**

LARGE, JUICY **JAPANESE** PLUMS ARE THE ONES WE usually eat out of hand in the summer months. They make superbly thirst-quenching snacks and desserts and are excellent raw in savory salads, fruit salads, and salsas. For baking and stewing, however, you'll want to choose the smaller, firmer, and tarter **European** plums; these excellent cooking fruits come in a variety of colors, from green to red to purple and blue-black.

CHOOSING & STORING

* Look for skins that are glossy and vividly colored; a blue-gray, powdery bloom is natural in most varieties and a sign of freshness.

* Ripe plums should be plump and should feel tender and a little bouncy when pressed with your fingertip.

* Taste a plum if possible before buying a lot; it can be difficult to tell a juicy, flavorful plum from a mealy or bland one without getting under the skin.

* Store ripe plums in the refrigerator for a few days; underripe plums will soften if stored at room temperature for a few days but will not become sweeter.

GOOD FOR YOU

The skins of purple and black plums are an excellent source of antioxidants, including chlorogenic acid.

TASTE TIPS

* The skins of plums are generally more sour than their flesh; although this is usually a pleasant contrast, peeling the fruit is advisable for some dishes, especially cooked ones.

* Peel plums neatly by scoring the bottom of each fruit with a small X, dropping it into boiling water for 15 seconds, and then transferring it to a bowl of cold water to cool. You should be able to remove the skin with your fingers or gently scrape it off with the back of a paring knife.

* Slice plums over cereal, yogurt, or ice cream. Sprinkle them with a little cinnamon or ground ginger to heighten their natural spicy flavor.

* Grill or sauté plums quickly and serve them with meats, poultry, or tofu; their flavor goes well with thyme, rosemary, shallots, and soy sauce.

Plum Shortcake

Plum Salad with Apple and Walnuts

Toss 1 cup trimmed water-cress, 1 medium pitted and sliced plum, and 1 small cored and chopped Granny Smith apple in bowl. Sprinkle with 2 teaspoons balsamic vinegar and top with 1 tablespoon chopped toasted walnuts.

4 PointsPlus value

Poached Stone Fruit

Bring ½ cup water, 1 medium pitted and sliced plum, 1 medium pitted and sliced nectarine, 1 (2-inch) piece sliced fresh ginger, 1 piece star anise, and 1 teaspoon sugar to boil in skillet. Simmer, uncovered, until fruit is soft and sauce thickens slightly, 6–8 minutes. Discard ginger and star

4 PointsPlus value

Plum Shortcake

Toss 1 medium pitted and sliced plum with 1 tablespoon lemon juice, 1 teaspoon sugar, and pinch ground cardamom in small bowl; let stand 10 minutes. Spoon plum mixture over 1 (1½-ounce) sponge cake dessert shell and top with 1 tablespoon vanilla fat-free

5 PointsPlus value

Pomegranates

IN SEASON **October to January**

THE TOUGH, LEATHERY EXTERIOR OF A POMEGRANATE hides hundreds of tiny jewel-like seeds, each bursting with bracing, tart-sweet juice. There are a few impediments to getting to these delectable treats, it's true, but anyone who perseveres will be richly rewarded.

CHOOSING & STORING

* Hefting a few pomegranates will pay off: Fruit that feels heavy for its size is likely to be packed with juicy seeds.

* Look for pomegranates with vibrant, slightly glossy, plump skin with no sign of shrinking or wrinkling.

* Pomegranates are beautiful in a fruit bowl or as a centerpiece, but store them at room temperature for no more than a few days since they dry out quickly.

* Place pomegranates in a plastic bag and refrigerate for several weeks.

GOOD FOR YOU

Pomegranate seeds are a good source of vitamin C, potassium, folate, and vitamin K.

POMEGRANATE PREP 101

* Cut off the crown of the pomegranate, slicing though the skin and white pith but not into the seed cavity.

* Score the exterior into quarters, again cutting deeply through the skin and pith but not into the seeds.

* Drop the fruit into a large bowl of cold water and let it soak for 5 minutes. Holding the fruit below the surface of the water, break it into quarters along the lines you've scored and then bend the skin and membrane away from the seeds.

* You can nibble the seeds away from the membrane, or if you want to separate them for use in recipes, work underwater again to carefully pry them out with your fingers. The seeds should sink and be easy to scoop up; any white membrane should float to the top and is easily discarded.

* Scatter seeds over salads, drop into seltzer or other drinks, use as a garnish for pork and poultry dishes, or sprinkle over ice cream or other desserts.

Pomegranate and Orange Salad

Whisk together 1 tablespoon lemon juice, 1 teaspoon olive oil, and 1 teaspoon chopped fresh mint. Peel 1 orange and cut crosswise into ¼-inch slices. Arrange slices on plate and top with ¼ cup thinly sliced red onion, ¼ cup pomegranate seeds, and 4 pitted and chopped oil-cured black olives. Drizzle with dressing.

Pomegranate Breakfast Couscous

Pomegranate Breakfast Couscous

Stir ¼ cup light vanilla soy milk and ¼ teaspoon almond extract into 1 cup cooked warm whole wheat couscous. Top with ¼ cup pomegranate seeds and 1½ teaspoons sliced almonds.

Chocolate-Pomegranate Drops

Place 2 tablespoons semisweet chocolate chips in medium microwavable bowl; microwave on High, stirring every 15 seconds, until melted and smooth, 30 seconds–1 minute; cool slightly. Stir in ¼ cup pomegranate seeds until well coated. Drop by 6 heaping teaspoonfuls onto wax paper–lined plate. Refrigerate until chocolate is set, about 15 minutes.

Potatoes

IN SEASON **Year-round**

WHEN IT COMES TO POTATOES, THERE'S NO DOUBT THAT odd colors, small sizes, and quirky shapes are in. Petite varieties with off-beat characteristics were once the province of small growers and were sold almost exclusively at farmers' markets or to high-end restaurants. Today, however, they're being harvested in ever-increasing numbers and are showing up everywhere from supermarkets to warehouse clubs. But remember, you can't always judge a book by its cover, and the plain brown exterior of familiar russets can also yield a sublime potato experience.

CHOOSING & STORING

∗ Potatoes should feel firm, never rubbery or dried out.

∗ Skins should be uniformly colored and free of blotches, cracks, or soft spots.

∗ Avoid potatoes with a green cast to their skin; this is a sign of age or improper storage and may indicate the presence of solanine, a mild toxin.

∗ Never buy sprouted potatoes; their flavor and texture will be compromised.

∗ Store potatoes in a cool, dark place away from moisture. A basket is ideal for allowing good air circulation, important for maintaining freshness. Properly harvested and stored potatoes should last several weeks.

∗ Check stored potatoes periodically and remove any that show signs of softening, wrinkling, or sprouting—one bad one really can spoil the bunch.

∗ Potatoes concentrate pesticides in their skins, so if you like to eat potatoes in their jackets consider buying organically grown ones.

POTATO NOTES

Potatoes are broken loosely into categories based on their cooking qualities. **Floury potatoes** are low in sugar, high in starch, and cook up light and fluffy. **Waxy potatoes,** on the other hand, are lower in starch and higher in sugar and cook up firm and moist. And then there are **sweet potatoes:** Although similar in growing habits and appearance to regular potatoes, sweets are not closely related. "Yam" is also a misnomer, since true yams are tropical tubers with dry, bland flesh. We take the liberty of including sweet potatoes here since their selection and cooking qualities are so similar to those of regular potatoes.

Potatoes

Fingerlings

Small, long, sometimes bumpy potatoes in a variety of skin and flesh colors; generally firm and flavorful

BEST FOR
Steaming, roasting whole, boiling, salads

GOOD TO KNOW
Generally of excellent flavor and texture; best to prepare them in dishes that will highlight their unique shape

New

Any variety of potato harvested when still young and immature

BEST FOR
Steaming, roasting whole or halved, boiling, salads

GOOD TO KNOW
Most, but not all, new potatoes are waxy varieties; red-skinned are the most widely available of this type

Purple

Deep-purple or blue-black skin and purple flesh that turns violet or violet-gray with cooking; texture varies, but is usually dry and floury

BEST FOR
Roasting, boiling, mashing, grating, salads

GOOD TO KNOW
Of ancient origin, but newly popular in today's markets

Red-skinned

Deep red to dusty pink skins and white to ivory flesh; texture is firm and waxy

BEST FOR
Steaming, boiling, baking, mashing, salads, casseroles

GOOD TO KNOW
An excellently firm and full-flavored choice for classic potato salad

Russet

Generally large and oblong with rough, brown, sometimes scaly skin and lots of eyes; floury flesh that turns light and tender with cooking

BEST FOR
Baking, mashing, frying, casseroles

GOOD TO KNOW
Also known as baking potatoes and Idaho potatoes; a top choice for baking whole and for fluffy mashed potatoes

Sweet

Generally large and oblong with red, orange, or beige skin and ivory, yellow, or orange flesh; very sweet, moist, and complexly flavored

BEST FOR
Steaming, roasting, boiling, baking, mashing, frying, casseroles

GOOD TO KNOW
Sometimes incorrectly called a yam

White

Round, small to large, with thin tan skin and bright white flesh; moderately waxy flesh

BEST FOR
Boiling, mashing, casseroles, soups and stews

GOOD TO KNOW
Waxy but still tender texture make these a top choice for adding to soups and stews

Yellow

Round, small to medium potatoes with tan skins and yellow to deep golden flesh; waxy and flavorful when cooked

BEST FOR
Steaming, roasting, boiling, baking, mashing, salads, casseroles

GOOD TO KNOW
Common varieties include Yukon gold and Yellow Finn; both are excellent choices for mashed potatoes and potato salad

Potatoes

Curry-Roasted Baby Potatoes

Preheat oven to 400°F. Toss 4 ounces whole baby potatoes (4–5 potatoes) with 1 teaspoon olive oil, 1 teaspoon curry powder, ⅛ teaspoon ground ginger, and ⅛ teaspoon salt. Spread evenly in small baking pan and roast until tender, about 30 minutes. Sprinkle with 1 sliced scallion during last 5 minutes of cooking.

Potato and Greens Scramble

Cook ½ small chopped onion in 1 teaspoon olive oil in skillet until soft, about 5 minutes. Dice 1 small cooked red potato. Add potato and 1 cup baby spinach to skillet, stirring until spinach begins to wilt, 1–2 minutes. Add 2 large egg whites, ¼ teaspoon salt, and few drops hot sauce. Cook, stirring, until scrambled.

Sweet Potato, Apple, and Ham Salad

Combine 1 small peeled and sliced cooked sweet potato, ½ small cored and sliced Granny Smith apple, ½ sliced green bell pepper, ¼ cup diced lean ham, and 1 tablespoon chopped fresh chives in bowl. Toss with 2 teaspoons apple cider vinegar, 1 teaspoon olive oil, ¼ teaspoon salt, and pinch cayenne pepper.

GOOD FOR YOU

Both sweet and white potatoes are delicious sources of fiber, potassium, and manganese. Sweet potatoes also hold the distinction of being the best food source of vitamin A: One medium sweet potato has 21,900 IU, more than 400 percent of your daily requirement. Whatever type of potato you're eating, ditch the peeler—potato skins have the lion's share of this vegetable's fiber and phytochemicals.

Sweet Potato, Apple, and Ham Salad

RADI
RASPB
SP
STRAW
TOM

Radishes

CRISP, PUNGENT, TONGUE-TINGLING RADISHES ADD COLOR and zing to everything from salads to sandwiches to breakfast plates, and die-hard radish fans even sauté them. The most popular variety for salads and snacking are hot-pink or crimson radishes known variously as **spring radishes, summer radishes,** and **table radishes.** Most radishes are small and round, but a few varieties like **French breakfast** and **icicle** are elongated in shape and appear later in the season. A favorite in Asian cuisines is **daikon,** a huge, juicy, sweet radish that's good for pickling and soups and salads. **Black radishes** have snow-white, peppery flesh that's excellent for cooking.

CHOOSING & STORING

* Check attached greenery to see that it looks fresh and sprightly.

* Radishes should be very firm and heavy; softness or a light feeling may mean they're pithy and mealy, not crisp, inside.

* Remove greenery and refrigerate radishes in a plastic bag for up to 1 week.

GOOD FOR YOU

One cup of sliced radishes has a full 2 g of dietary fiber and almost a third of your daily requirement for vitamin C.

WHAT CHEFS KNOW

* For added crispness, trim radishes, cover with ice water, and refrigerate for an hour or two.

* Peel radishes if you want a milder flavor; their heat is concentrated in the skin.

* Try cooking with radishes; they're excellent sautéed or stewed with other vegetables, particularly spring vegetables. They can be cooked any way you would cook small turnips.

* Small baby radishes make a beautiful addition to spring crudité platters (leave the delicate greens on). Rounds of larger daikon or black radishes can be used as dippers year-round.

Radish and Snow Pea Sauté

Spiced Radish and Asian Pear Salad

Toss together 1 cored and chopped Asian pear and ½ cup sliced radishes in bowl with 1 tablespoon chopped pickled ginger, 1 tablespoon chopped fresh cilantro, 1 tablespoon lime juice, ½ small seeded and minced jalapeño pepper, and ½ teaspoon garam masala.

Radish and Snow Pea Sauté

Sauté 1 small sliced shallot and 1 minced garlic clove in 1 teaspoon butter in skillet until soft, about 1 minute. Add ½ cup halved radishes and ½ cup snow peas and cook until radishes are crisp-tender, 1–2 minutes. Stir in 1 tablespoon chopped fresh dill and pinch each salt and red pepper flakes.

Radish and Salmon Lettuce Wrap

Stir together ½ cup drained canned salmon, 2 tablespoons chopped radishes, 2 tablespoons plain fat-free Greek yogurt, 1 tablespoon chopped fresh dill, and 1 tablespoon lemon juice in small bowl. Thinly slice ¼ small cucumber. Divide salmon mixture between two Boston lettuce leaves. Top with cucumber slices and roll up.

Raspberries

IN SEASON June to September

RASPBERRIES MAKE THEMSELVES AT HOME WITH SOME of the world's most luxurious ingredients, including champagne and chocolate, but they often shine brightest when matched with humbler fare such as yogurt, oatmeal, or even a simple salad. Red berries are the norm, but **golden** and **black** raspberries are also available; both varieties can have a deeper, sweeter flavor than standard berries, but taste them before paying a premium to avoid disappointment.

CHOOSING & STORING

* Select deeply colored raspberries with no signs of bruising or mold.

* Check that raspberries are not still attached to the stem, a sign that they were harvested while still unripe and will be sour.

* Refrigerate berries for no more than 2 or 3 days to prevent molding; remove any damaged berries immediately, or they may affect the rest.

GOOD FOR YOU

Raspberries are packed with fiber and vitamin C and contain a number of antioxidants, including ellagic acid.

TASTE TIPS

* Add instant glamour to seltzer, ice tea, lemonade, or sparkling wine by dropping a few berries into your glass.

* Use raspberries as a garnish for salads, poultry, or pork dishes.

* Combine a few mashed raspberries and $1/2$ cup champagne vinegar or rice wine vinegar in a glass jar; refrigerate for a few days and you'll have delicious raspberry vinegar.

Fresh Corn, Crab, and Raspberry Salad

3 PointsPlus® value

Raspberry Parfait

Combine ¼ cup fat-free ricotta cheese with 1 teaspoon grated orange zest, 1 teaspoon confectioners' sugar, and ¼ teaspoon cinnamon in small bowl. Cut 1 large ladyfinger into 4 pieces and place in dessert bowl; drizzle with 1 tablespoon orange juice. Spoon ricotta mixture over top and sprinkle with ¼ cup raspberries.

4 PointsPlus® value

Crushed Raspberry Fool

Swirl 1 tablespoon prepared lemon curd into ½ cup plain fat-free Greek yogurt in small bowl. Toss ½ cup raspberries with 1 teaspoon lemon juice and ½ teaspoon sugar in medium bowl; let stand 5 minutes. Lightly crush raspberries with fork and spoon over yogurt.

4 PointsPlus® value

Fresh Corn, Crab, and Raspberry Salad

Combine ½ cup raspberries, ½ cup corn kernels, ¼ cup cooked crabmeat, 1 tablespoon minced red onion, and 1 tablespoon seasoned rice vinegar in bowl; toss gently to mix. Sprinkle with 1 tablespoon chopped fresh basil.

Spinach

IN SEASON **March through May**
& September through October

SPINACH HAS BEEN CELEBRATED BY SUCH DIVERSE characters as Catherine de Medici, who insisted it be served at every meal, and Popeye, who ate it to build shirt-popping muscles. Native to Persia, this high-profile vegetable traveled to China by way of India in the seventh century but didn't reach Europe until almost 500 years later. Its popularity quickly spread, and today it is widely available and prized for its flavor, versatility, and excellent nutritional profile.

CHOOSING & STORING

* Look for deep green leaves that are firm and crisp. Avoid leaves that are yellowed, bruised, or slimy.

* For salads choose small tender leaves. Reserve larger leaves with thicker stems for cooking.

* Do not wash spinach before storing. Dry the leaves if they are damp and store in a perforated plastic bag in the refrigerator. Spinach will keep for 3 to 4 days.

GOOD FOR YOU

Spinach is one of the most nutrient-dense foods on the planet. In addition to being rich in vitamins A, C, and K and a good source of potassium and fiber, it contains a number of antioxidants.

WHAT CHEFS KNOW

* Because it's grown in sandy soil, spinach needs to be thoroughly washed before using. Separate the spinach into leaves, trim the stems, and remove and discard any large ribs. Immerse the leaves in a big bowl or sink of water, agitating them to remove sand. Lift the spinach out of the water (the silt should remain at the bottom of the bowl or sink), and repeat washings once or twice more, or until leaves are thoroughly clean.

* Avoid using aluminum pans when cooking spinach as aluminum adversely affects its color and taste.

* Drain spinach thoroughly after cooking to avoid puddles of liquid on your plate or watery recipes.

* One pound of spinach when cooked will yield about 1 cup, serving 2.

Spinach

Sautéed Spinach with Parmesan Bread Crumbs

Cook 3 cups baby spinach in 1 tablespoon water in skillet over medium-high heat until wilted, about 2 minutes. Toss with 1 tablespoon whole wheat bread crumbs, 1 teaspoon grated Parmesan cheese, 1 teaspoon olive oil, and pinch each salt and pepper until spinach is well coated, about 1 minute.

Spinach and Sweet Potato Salad with Orange Vinaigrette

Whisk together 1 tablespoon orange juice, 2 teaspoons apple cider vinegar, 1 teaspoon olive oil, and ½ teaspoon Dijon mustard in large bowl. Add 2 cups baby spinach, ½ small diced cooked sweet potato, and 1 tablespoon golden raisins and toss.

Spinach and Curried Egg Salad Wrap

Finely chop 1 large hard-cooked egg and mash in bowl with ¼ cup drained soft tofu, 1 tablespoon fat-free mayonnaise, 1 teaspoon curry powder, and pinch each salt and pepper until well mixed. Spread on 1 small fat-free tortilla. Top with 1 cup baby spinach and roll up.

Spinach and Curried Egg Salad Wrap

Strawberries

IN SEASON **April to July**

HERALDING AN END TO THE DARK DAYS OF WINTER and the arrival of spring, the emergence at markets of juicy, aromatic, ruby-red strawberries is a welcome sign of good things to come. During berry season, be sure to look out for **wild strawberries** at farmers' markets—these small wonders are a revelation in sweetness and flavor.

CHOOSING & STORING

* Choose strawberries that are firm, free of mold, and deep red with fresh green caps.

* Avoid berries that have green or white patches around the stem—a sure sign they are not fully ripe. Once picked, berries do not continue to ripen.

* If purchasing berries in packages, check that they are not so tightly packed they have bruised. Likewise, check the bottom of the container for any excess moisture or staining.

* To store, remove berries from the container and discard any that are damaged. Return the unwashed, unhulled berries to the container or spread them out on a paper towel-lined plate and loosely cover with plastic. Refrigerate berries for up to 2 days.

* Berries freeze well. Gently rinse, pat dry, and arrange them on a tray in a single layer. Freeze until firm and transfer to a freezer bag. Frozen berries will keep for 8 to 10 months.

TASTE TIPS

* Gently rinse and hull berries just before serving, drain, and pat dry. If serving whole, you may leave the caps intact.

* To revitalize the flavor of tired berries, sprinkle with 1 teaspoon each sugar and fresh lemon juice per cup. Let sit for 20 minutes at room temperature.

* Strawberries are delicious "au naturel" simply dusted with sugar. The classic accompaniment to fresh strawberries is cream, but yogurt is equally satisfying.

* Not only are strawberries wonderful in fruit salads, but you can add them to leafy green salads and toss with a light balsamic dressing.

* Strawberries add flavor and eye appeal to cereals, pancakes, waffles, cakes, and frozen desserts.

* Strawberries are ideal in sorbets, frozen yogurts, parfaits, smoothies, cold soups, tarts, and dessert sauces and as a filling for shortcakes.

Strawberries

Strawberry and Endive Salad with Goat Cheese and Pine Nuts

Separate leaves of 1 small endive and arrange on plate. Top with 1 cup sliced strawberries; drizzle with 2 teaspoons balsamic vinegar. Sprinkle with 1 tablespoon soft goat cheese, crumbled, and 1 teaspoon toasted pine nuts.

Strawberry and Ice Cream Waffle Sandwich

Dice 2 medium strawberries and mix with 2 tablespoons slightly softened vanilla fat-free frozen yogurt. Spread on 1 frozen toasted mini waffle and top with another toasted waffle. Gently press together. Wrap in wax paper and freeze until firm, about 1 hour.

Orecchiette with Strawberries and Chicken

Combine ½ cup sliced strawberries, ½ small chopped unpeeled apple, ¼ cup cubed cooked chicken, and ¼ cup cooked whole wheat orecchiette or other small pasta in bowl. Toss with 2 tablespoons fat-free poppy seed dressing.

GOOD FOR YOU

Strawberries contain about 55 calories per cup and provide unusually high amounts of vitamin C. One cup contains 90 mg of vitamin C, more than the recommended daily intake for an adult. They also boast fiber and potassium and a number of potent antioxidants.

Tomatoes

IN SEASON July to October

THE TOMATO IS A STUDY IN CONTRADICTIONS: IS IT A fruit or a vegetable, poison or aphrodisiac? Botanically a fruit but widely accepted as a vegetable, the tomato originated in the Andean regions of South America, eventually finding its way to North America over 2,000 years ago. Because of the strong odor of their foliage and association with the nightshade family, they initially were thought to be poisonous. Yet once the Italians popularized them and the French dubbed them "love apples" (crediting them with aphrodisiac qualities), they became a favored ingredient.

CHOOSING & STORING

* Choose firm—not hard—deeply colored tomatoes that are fragrant and heavy for their size. Avoid tomatoes that are bruised and soft.

* Do not refrigerate whole ripe tomatoes. Store them at room temperature away from sunlight for 3 to 4 days.

* If they are unripe, put tomatoes in a paper bag with an apple. The ethylene gas given off by the apple will speed up the ripening process.

* Once cut, tomatoes should be wrapped in plastic and placed in the refrigerator.

TO PEEL OR NOT TO PEEL?

* Raw tomatoes are almost always eaten with the skin left intact: the skin is a concentrated source of fiber and nutrients, and also helps slices and wedges of tomato hold their shape.

* For some cooked dishes, such as homemade tomato sauce and stews or braises that are simmered for a while, it's advisable to peel them as heat toughens the skin.

* To peel, use a sharp, preferably serrated knife and cut an X at the base of the tomato. Blanch it in boiling water for 20 to 30 seconds, or until the edges of the X begin to curl. Transfer to a bowl of cold water to cool and then slip off the peel.

* To seed tomatoes, slice them in half horizontally and use your fingers to scoop out and discard the seeds.

Tomatoes

Beefsteak

Big, meaty, deep red slicing tomatoes; rich and tangy

BEST FOR
Salads, slicing, sauce, baking, stuffing

GOOD TO KNOW
Classic slicing tomato with reliably good flavor and texture in season

Cherry

Small, red-orange to red; sweet, juicy and aromatic

BEST FOR
Snacking, salads

GOOD TO KNOW
A real treat at their best, but can be bland outside of tomato season; yellow, green, or orange varieties sometimes available

Grape

Small, red, firm; mild flavor

BEST FOR
Snacking, salads

GOOD TO KNOW
Can be bland outside of tomato season

Green

Unripe tomatoes, very firm and tart

BEST FOR
Roasting, baking, grilling, pickling

GOOD TO KNOW
Generally considered too tart to eat raw, but excellent for everything from pan-frying to grilling

Heirloom

Variable shapes and flavors and a rainbow of colors

BEST FOR
Salads, slicing, snacks, stuffing

GOOD TO KNOW
Hundreds of unique varieties available from growers large and small; flavors can vary from sweet to tangy to fruity to bland

Hydroponic

Medium-sized, bright red; juicy, with mild to deep flavor and tang

BEST FOR
Sauce, roasting, baking, stuffing

GOOD TO KNOW
Also known as vine tomatoes; versatility and fairly reliable flavor make them a good choice outside of tomato season

Kumato

Medium-sized, dark brown to green; firm, juicy, and sweet

BEST FOR
Salads, slicing

GOOD TO KNOW
Greenhouse grown variety developed for good flavor and long shelf life; good choice outside of tomato season

Plum

Medium-sized light to bright red; very firm with mild flavor

BEST FOR
Sauce, roasting

GOOD TO KNOW
Also known as Roma; good choice for cooking outside of tomato season, especially when roasted to concentrate flavor

Yellow

Medium to large, bright yellow to orange; very sweet, fruity and juicy with low acid

BEST FOR
Salads, slicing, sauce, roasting, stuffing

GOOD TO KNOW
Most yellow tomatoes are exceptionally sweet; very attractive when mixed with other tomato colors

Yellow grape

Small, yellow to orange, firm; sweet and mildly flavored

BEST FOR
Snacking, salads

GOOD TO KNOW
Very attractive when mixed with other tomato colors

Tomatoes

Stuffed Tomato Salad

Scoop out pulp from 1 large halved tomato. Combine ¼ cup cubed fat-free mozzarella cheese, 1 tablespoon minced red onion, 1 tablespoon chopped fresh basil, and 2 teaspoons fat-free vinaigrette in small bowl. Divide mozzarella mixture between tomato shells.

Creamy Chilled Tomato Soup

Puree 1 large chopped tomato with 1 cup low-sodium tomato juice, 1 tablespoon balsamic vinegar, ¼ cup fat-free plain yogurt, and 1 tablespoon chopped fresh dill in food processor or blender until smooth. Refrigerate until chilled.

Cherry Tomatoes with Angel-Hair Pasta and Herbs

Combine 1 cup halved cherry tomatoes, 1 tablespoon chopped fresh oregano, 1 teaspoon drained capers, and 1 teaspoon olive oil in medium bowl. Stir in ½ cup cooked whole wheat angel hair pasta or other thin whole wheat spaghetti and sprinkle with 1 teaspoon grated Parmesan cheese.

GOOD FOR YOU

Tomatoes are an excellent source of vitamins A and C, potassium, and dietary fiber. They also contain significant amounts of lycopene and beta-carotene, antioxidants that may promote health and prevent disease.

Stuffed Tomato Salad

WATER
W
ZUCC

MELON
NTER
SQUASH
HINI

Watermelon

IN SEASON June to August

IT'S NO SURPRISE THAT WATERMELON, THE QUINTESSEN-tial sweet and cooling antidote to the dog days of summer, originated in Africa, where it was prized not only for its flavor but also as a source of hydration. In the New World, Native Americans and settlers fully embraced this versatile melon, cultivating over 50 varieties. Watermelons range in size from small round ones like **Sugar Baby** to giant elongated ones like **Charleston Gray.** Seedless varieties have become overwhelmingly popular, but seeds are so easy to remove that you should let flavor and ripeness be your guide when selecting a melon.

CHOOSING & STORING

* Look for smooth, unblemished skin with deep color. One side of the melon may be paler than the rest, indicating that part of the rind was resting on the ground while ripening on the vine.

* Fragrance is important; a ripe melon should smell fresh and sweet. When tapped, it should sound taut and hollow if ripe.

* If you purchase a piece of a cut watermelon, look for firm flesh with deep color and dark seeds.

* Before storing or cutting watermelon, rinse the exterior well under cold running water.

* You can store whole watermelon at room temperature for 7 to 10 days or in the refrigerator for 2 to 3 weeks.

* Store cut melon in covered containers or covered with plastic wrap in the refrigerator and use within 2 to 3 days.

TASTE TIPS

* Once cut, watermelon is best eaten as soon as possible. It's most refreshing when served chilled.

* Made up of 92 percent water, it's ideal for frozen desserts like ices, sorbets, and granitas.

* Pureed watermelon combines well with other fruit juices and yogurt to make tasty smoothies and with seltzer and lime for a thirst-quench-ing drink. It also lends itself to summer soups.

* Watermelon pairs well with fresh mint, cilantro, fresh chiles, bell pepper, and cucumber to make a refreshing salsa.

GOOD FOR YOU

Watermelon is a good source of vitamins A and C and the antioxidant lycopene.

Watermelon Gazpacho

Place 1 cup cubed seedless watermelon, ½ small chopped tomato, ¼ seeded and diced cucumber, ¼ red bell pepper, ½ seeded and minced jalapeño pepper, 2 tablespoons red-wine vinegar, and pinch each salt and pepper in blender and puree. Cover and refrigerate until chilled.

Watermelon with Arugula and Prosciutto

Pile 1 cup baby arugula onto plate. Top with 1 cup cubed cold seedless watermelon and ½ (1-ounce) slice prosciutto cut into thin strips; drizzle with 1 teaspoon olive oil and sprinkle with 1 tablespoon chopped fresh mint and pinch black pepper.

Watermelon Stack

Arrange ½ small tomato cut into ¼-inch slices on plate. Top with 2 slices seedless, rindless watermelon. Sprinkle with 1 tablespoon crumbled reduced-fat feta cheese, 1 tablespoon chopped fresh mint, 2 teaspoons lime juice, 1 teaspoon olive oil, and pinch each salt and black pepper.

Watermelon Stack

Winter Squash

NO OTHER VEGETABLE USHERS IN THE COOLER MONTHS like winter squash. From burnt orange pumpkins ripening on the vine to the colorful, oddly-shaped varieties found on market stands, the arrival of these festive vegetables each fall is a welcome sign of the change of seasons. Unlike their summer counterparts, zucchini and yellow squash, winter squash require cooking and are rarely eaten raw.

CHOOSING & STORING

* Look for squash that have hard unblemished skin. Unless the skin itself is green, it should not contain any pale or dark green spots, an indication of immaturity.

* The shell should be neither shiny nor dull. It should have a matte finish.

* Stems should be firm, dry, and sturdy, not skinny and limp. Avoid purchasing pumpkins without stems.

* Check to see where the squash was grown. Squash from cooler climates will have developed more slowly and have better flavor; the longer on the vine, the sweeter and more flavorful the flesh.

* When purchasing squash that has been cut up, look for slightly moist, tight-grained flesh without fibers.

* If stored in a cool, well-ventilated, dry area, whole squash will keep for months. Or store on the counter for several weeks. (They'll look lovely there, too.) There is no need to refrigerate whole squash.

SAFE HANDLING

Because of their hard shells and large size, cutting winter squash requires special care. Here's how to play it safe:

* Select a heavy, preferably serrated knife or cleaver. A rubber mallet is also a helpful tool.

* Place the squash on a towel to prevent it from sliding around, and cut it next to, not through, the stem.

* Insert the tip of the knife into the squash and work it down the side, using the mallet to hit the knife into the squash until it is split open.

* Alternatively, bake the squash whole until it is just softened; cut it open, remove the seeds, and continue baking until cooked through. Be sure to pierce a whole squash in a number of places before baking to prevent it from bursting open in the oven.

Winter Squash

Acorn

Small, with ridged green or green and orange exterior and sweet, dense, slightly fibrous flesh

BEST FOR
Baking, roasting, steaming

GOOD TO KNOW
A very hard, deeply ridged shell makes it difficult to peel when raw; peel after cooking if your recipe requires it

Butternut

Medium-sized, smooth, buff-colored and bell-shaped, with very smooth, buttery, sweet, nutty flesh

BEST FOR
Baking, roasting, steaming, purees, soups

GOOD TO KNOW
Smooth skin and abundant flesh make it ideal for peeling and cutting into chunks for steaming, boiling, and roasting; top choice for making soups and purees

Calabaza

Medium to large, with mottled green to orange skin and lightly sweet, fresh-tasting flesh that can be watery

BEST FOR
Roasting, purees, soups

GOOD TO KNOW
Also known as West Indian pumpkin; grown in warm climates, so available year-round

Carnival

Very colorful, striped to speckled skin with deep ridges; sweet, rich, dense flesh

BEST FOR
Baking, steaming

GOOD TO KNOW
A cross between an acorn squash and a dumpling squash; flamboy-antly colored skin and good flavor make it ideal for halving and baking

Delicata

Small and oblong with festive stripes; creamy, very sweet, dense flesh with a caramel-like flavor

BEST FOR
Baking, steaming, purees

GOOD TO KNOW
One of the tastiest small, single-serving squashes available

Hubbard

Medium to very large, with thick blue to green or deep-orange skin; sweet, smooth flesh

BEST FOR
Baking, roasting, stewing, purees, soups

GOOD TO KNOW
Very large Hubbards are extremely decorative but may have skin so tough that cutting into them becomes difficult

Kabocha

Small to medium, with blue-green to orange skin; very smooth, deeply flavored, honey-sweet flesh

BEST FOR
Baking, roasting, steaming, purees, soups

GOOD TO KNOW
Sometimes called Japanese pumpkin

Miniature pumpkin

Tiny, slightly flattened orange to cream-colored and deeply ridged; nutty, sweet, tender flesh

BEST FOR
Baking, steaming

GOOD TO KNOW
One of the smallest winter squash, ideal for individual servings; looks really festive on the counter too

Pumpkin

Small to very large, with ridged, thick skin; sweet and creamy or bland and watery depending on variety

BEST FOR
Purees

GOOD TO KNOW
Avoid disappointment by cooking only with "pie pumpkins." Sugar Baby and Sweetie Pie are two common varieties with good flavor and firmer texture

Spaghetti

Buttery yellow squash with very mild, lightly sweet flesh that separates into long strands after cooking

BEST FOR
Roasting, steaming

GOOD TO KNOW
Excellent topped with sauce, soaking up gravy, or tossed with herbs and olive oil or butter

Sweet dumpling

Very small with ridged skin; sweet, rich flesh

BEST FOR
Baking, steaming

GOOD TO KNOW
One of the smallest winter squashes, ideal for individual servings

Turban

Medium to large, with a round base and brilliantly colored "hat" on top; nutty, lightly sweet flesh

BEST FOR
Roasting, steaming

GOOD TO KNOW
A popular harvest ornament, but also edible, although its thick skin can be difficult to cut

Winter Squash

TASTE TIPS

* Squash is delicious roasted or baked, whole or halved. It lends itself to sautéing, grilling, and pureeing and is perfect in gratins, soups, stews, risottos, breads, cakes, and even pies.

* Squash seeds may be roasted and served as a healthy snack. Rinse seeds to remove flesh and pat dry. Spread the seeds in one layer on a parchment-lined baking sheet. Bake in a preheated 325°F oven until lightly toasted, about 15 minutes.

* Stuff smaller squash, such as acorn, and serve in its own shell. Likewise, miniature pumpkins make festive soup bowls for pumpkin soup.

* As an alternative to pasta, cooked strands of spaghetti squash pair well with a Bolognese sauce or with other vegetables, such as a primavera mixture in a light sauce.

* Pair squash with sage, rosemary, garlic, chili, cumin, ginger, nutmeg, curry, ginger, clove, lime, onions, garlic, apples, and cheeses.

GOOD FOR YOU

Winter squash is an excellent source of vitamins A and C as well as a good source of potassium. This vegetable's orange flesh is a sign that it's high in the antioxidant beta-carotene. Generally speaking, the deeper the color of a vegetable, the higher the beta-carotene content.

Roasted Butternut Squash with Pears

Preheat oven to 400°F. Combine 1 cup peeled and cubed butternut squash, 1 chopped small pear, and ½ sliced lemon on baking pan sprayed with nonstick spray. Drizzle with ¼ cup pear nectar and sprinkle with ¼ teaspoon salt. Roast, turning occasionally, until tender, 20–25 minutes.

Squash Soup with Apples and Leeks

Preheat oven to 400°F. Place ½ seeded medium acorn squash, cut side down, in small foil-lined baking pan. Roast until tender, about 30 minutes. Let cool slightly. Scoop out flesh and combine with 1½ cups fat-free low-sodium chicken broth, ½ chopped small apple, and ¼ cup sliced leeks in saucepan; cover and simmer until leeks are tender, about 15 minutes. Transfer soup and ¼ cup fat-free half-and-half to blender and puree. Sprinkle with grated nutmeg.

Spaghetti Squash Primavera

Sauté ¼ pound sliced mushrooms and 2 garlic cloves in 1 teaspoon olive oil in skillet, about 5 minutes. Add 1 chopped tomato, ½ cup sliced asparagus, ¼ cup frozen peas, and ⅔ cup fat-free chicken broth; simmer until tomato is soft and asparagus is tender, 2–3 minutes. Toss with 1 cup cooked spaghetti squash. Sprinkle with 1 tablespoon grated Parmesan.

Squash Soup with Apples and Leeks

Zucchini

IN SEASON **May to August**

THE JEWEL IN THE CROWN OF THE SUMMER SQUASH family, zucchini originated in the New World and together with corn and beans served as a basis for the cuisines of North American and South American Indians. Unlike its winter squash cousins, zucchini is eaten when it is young and tender and has not yet developed fully mature seeds. Other varieties of summer squash closely related to zucchini and interchangeable in most dishes include **yellow** squash, green-and-white striped **Neapolitan** squash, and small, flying saucer-shaped **patty pan** squash.

CHOOSING & STORING

* Bigger is not better. Small or medium-size zucchini are most flavorful. Look for zucchini that are 5 to 6 inches long and about 1 to 2 inches in diameter with at least 1 inch of stem still attached.

* The skin on zucchini should be smooth, shiny, and unblemished. The darker the skin, the richer the nutrients.

* A good zucchini will feel heavier than it looks.

* Store zucchini in a perforated plastic bag in the vegetable bin of the refrigerator for 4 to 5 days. It's best not to wash zucchini until you're ready to use it.

WHAT CHEFS KNOW

* An average zucchini, about 6 inches long, weighs between 4 and 6 ounces. Allow 1 1/2 pounds for four generous servings. One pound of squash yields approximately 4 cups grated or 3 1/2 cups diced or sliced.

* Both summer and winter squash produce edible flowers, but those sold at farmers' markets and food stores generally come from the zucchini plant. Prized by connoisseurs, these delicately flavored flowers can be used in numerous ways. Add them to soups and sautés; fold them into omelets, risottos, and pastas; or simply toss with summer greens and herbs for a refreshing salad. They're also delicious and beautiful when stuffed with ground meat, soft cheeses, fish, or cooked grains and baked, pan-fried, or steamed.

Zucchini

TASTE TIPS

* The versatility of zucchini is limitless. It's delicious grilled, baked, and broiled. Add it to stir-fries, soups, pastas, breads (sweet and savory), and even desserts. Cut it into ribbons to resemble pasta and serve it cooked or raw. It makes a perfect container for your favorite stuffing and even lends itself to being pickled.

* Since there's no need to peel or seed young zucchini, it's excellent for eating raw and in salads.

* To boost nutrition, add grated zucchini to your favorite dishes, such as macaroni and cheese, lasagna, and meatloaf. It's a great way to get more vegetables into your diet

GOOD FOR YOU

One cup of zucchini provides 35 percent of the recommended daily intake of vitamin C, 5 percent of vitamin A, and 2 percent each of calcium and iron. It's also low in sodium and contains heart-healthy potassium.

Zucchini and Ricotta Roll-Ups

Combine ¼ cup fat-free ricotta cheese, 1 tablespoon chopped sun-dried tomatoes (not oil-packed), 2 teaspoons grated lemon zest, and ¼ teaspoon black pepper in small bowl. With vegetable peeler, shave 4 lengthwise strips from ½ small zucchini into long ribbons. Spoon 1 tablespoon ricotta mixture onto each ribbon and roll up. Sprinkle with grated lemon zest, if desired.

Zucchini with Peas and Pesto

Steam 1 cup sliced zucchini and ¼ cup frozen peas until zucchini is crisp-tender, 3–4 minutes. Toss zucchini and peas in bowl with 1 tablespoon prepared pesto, 1 tablespoon grated Parmesan cheese, and pinch red pepper flakes.

Zucchini Pancakes

Grate 1 small (4-ounce) zucchini in bowl. Stir in 2 tablespoons plus 1 teaspoon white whole wheat flour, 1 large egg white, ½ teaspoon baking powder, and ¼ teaspoon salt until well mixed. Heat 1 teaspoon canola oil in large nonstick skillet over medium-high heat. Drop batter into skillet, making total of 3 pancakes. Cook until browned, 2–3 minutes per side. Serve with 2 tablespoons fat-free sour cream.

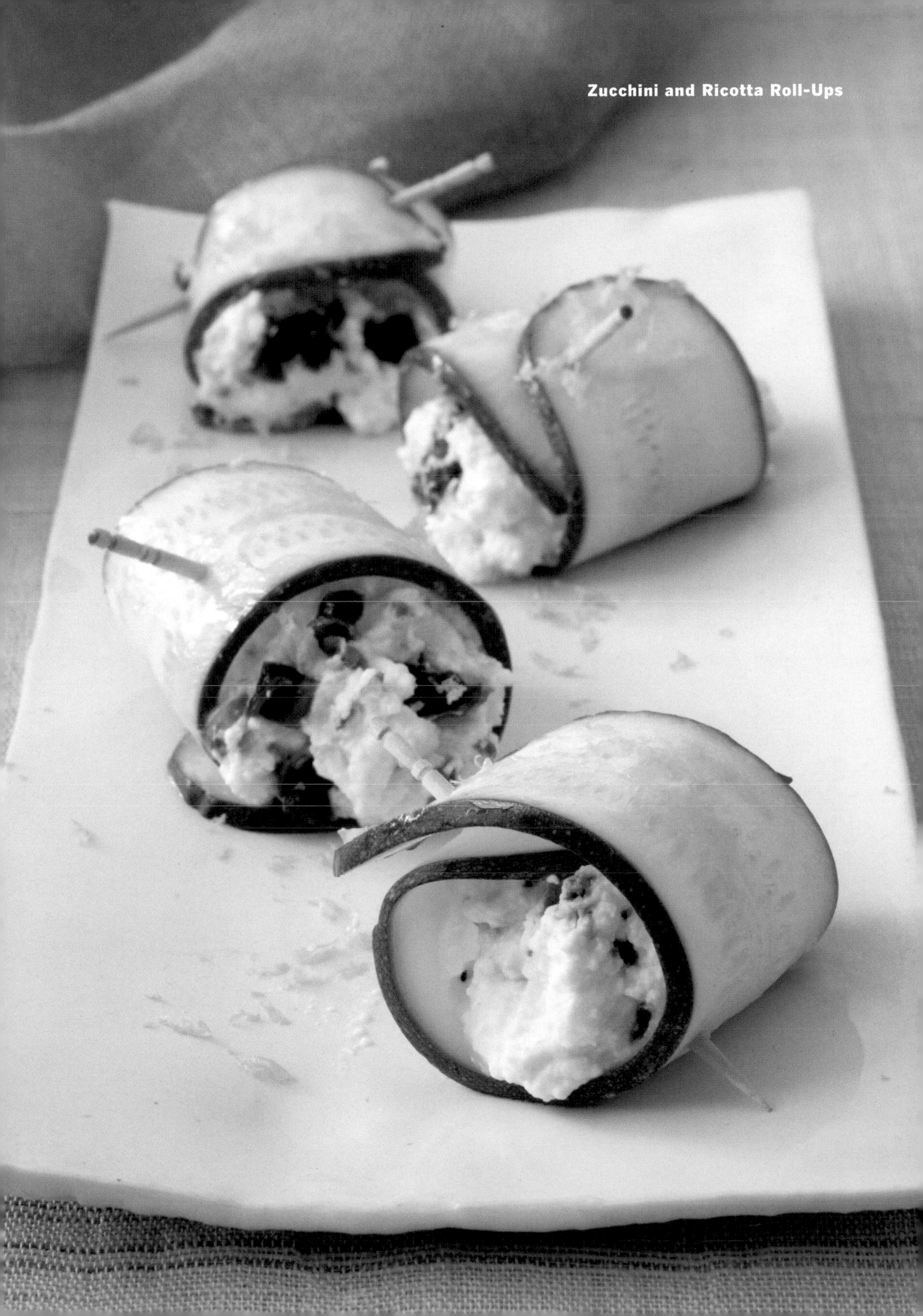
Zucchini and Ricotta Roll-Ups

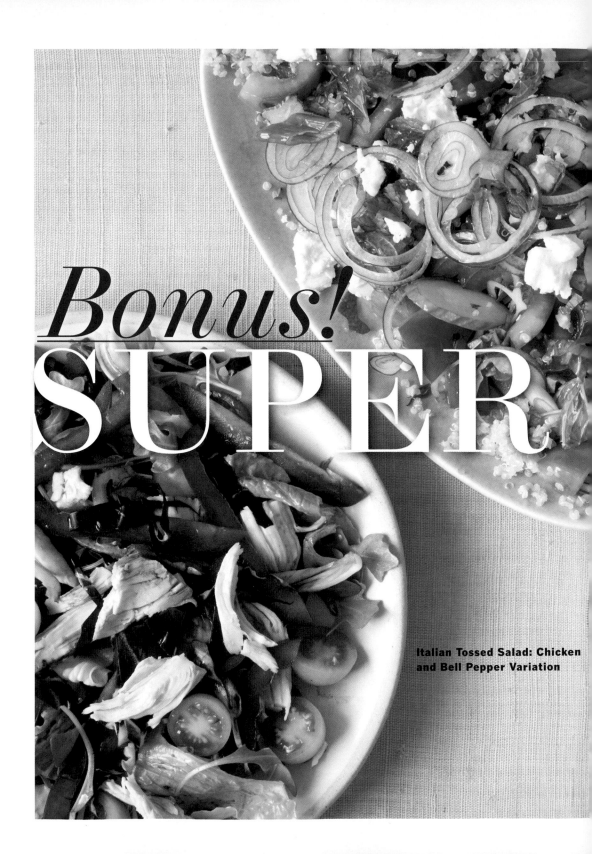

Bonus! SUPER

Italian Tossed Salad: Chicken and Bell Pepper Variation

Greek Salad: Quinoa
Tabbouleh Variation

SALADS

Tex-Mex Chopped Salad: Huevos
Rancheros Variation

Super Salads

Six all-time favorites, each with three easy, filling variations. Getting more crisp, fresh produce into your day has never been easier or tastier!

ITALIAN TOSSED SALAD

Red Onion and Parmesan Salad

Chickpea and Scallion Salad

Chicken and Bell Pepper Salad

GREEK SALAD

Spinach and Chickpea Salad

Stuffed Grape Leaves and Olive Salad

Quinoa Tabbouleh Salad

TEX-MEX CHOPPED SALAD

Bean and Pepper Jack Salad

Ground Turkey and Onion Salad

Huevos Rancheros Salad

CHINESE CABBAGE SALAD

Shrimp and Edamame Salad

Sesame Tofu Salad

Chinese Chicken Salad

SWEET AND SAVORY CALIFORNIA SALAD

Brown Rice Citrus Salad

Crabmeat Salad with Nectarine and Onion

Goat Cheese Salad with Almonds and Dates

RUSSIAN BEET AND CARROT SALAD

Beet Salad with Cucumber and Cottage Cheese

Beet Salad with Chopped Egg and Dill

Beet, Apple, and Walnut Salad

Italian Tossed Salad

Serves 1 (about 3 cups)

2 cups chopped romaine lettuce

1 cup baby arugula

$1/2$ small head radicchio, sliced

$1/2$ cup halved cherry tomatoes

1 tablespoon balsamic vinegar

1 teaspoon olive oil

$1/8$ teaspoon salt

$1/8$ teaspoon black pepper

Combine lettuce, arugula, radicchio, and tomatoes in large bowl. Sprinkle with vinegar, oil, salt, and pepper and toss to combine.

CHANGE IT UP

Red Onion and Parmesan Salad

Add $1/4$ cup sliced red onion and 3 or 4 sliced fresh basil leaves to the lettuce mixture. Serve the salad sprinkled with 2 tablespoons grated Parmesan cheese.

Chickpea and Scallion Salad

Add $1/3$ cup drained and rinsed canned chickpeas and 3 sliced scallions to the salad.

Chicken and Bell Pepper Salad

Add $1/2$ cup diced cooked skinless and boneless chicken breast and $1/2$ thinly sliced red bell pepper to the salad.

Greek Salad

Serves 1 (about 2 ½ cups)

2 tablespoons red-wine vinegar

1 teaspoon chopped fresh oregano or parsley

1 teaspoon olive oil

⅛ teaspoon salt

1 small tomato, chopped

½ green bell pepper, chopped

½ small cucumber, seeded and chopped

¼ small red onion, thinly sliced

2 tablespoons reduced-fat crumbled feta cheese

Combine vinegar, oregano, olive oil, and salt in large bowl; add tomato, bell pepper, cucumber, and onion; toss to mix well. Sprinkle with cheese.

CHANGE IT UP

Spinach and Chickpea Salad

Add 1 cup baby spinach, ¼ cup drained and rinsed canned chickpeas, and 1 tablespoon orange juice to the salad.

Stuffed Grape Leaves and Olive Salad

Add 2 stuffed grape leaves, 4 pitted and chopped kalamata olives, and 1 tablespoon chopped fresh dill to the salad.

Quinoa Tabbouleh Salad

Add ⅓ cup cooked quinoa, 2 thinly sliced scallions, 2 tablespoons chopped fresh mint, and 1 tablespoon lemon juice to the salad.

Tex-Mex Chopped Salad

Serves 1 (about 3 cups)

1 small Kirby cucumber, diced

4 scallions, thinly sliced

1/2 small jicama, peeled and diced

1/2 small green bell pepper, diced

1/3 cup sweet corn kernels

1/4 cup chopped fresh cilantro

1/3 cup fat-free salsa

1 tablespoon fat-free sour cream

Combine cucumber, scallions, jicama, bell pepper, corn, and cilantro in large bowl. Mix salsa and sour cream together in small bowl and pour over salad.

CHANGE IT UP

Bean and Pepper Jack Salad

Add 1/4 cup drained and rinsed canned pinto beans, 2 tablespoons shredded reduced-fat pepper Jack cheese, and 2 teaspoons lime juice to the salad.

Ground Turkey and Onion Salad

Sauté 3 ounces ground skinless turkey breast with 1/4 cup diced onion in small nonstick skillet over medium heat until browned. Stir in 1/4 teaspoon chili powder and pinch salt. Sprinkle over the salad.

Huevos Rancheros Salad

Top the salad with 1 large soft-cooked egg. Spoon the salsa and sour cream over top and sprinkle with 1 tablespoon shredded fat-free Cheddar cheese.

Chinese Cabbage Salad

Serves 1 (about 2 ½ cups)

2 tablespoons rice vinegar

1 tablespoon grated peeled fresh ginger

2 teaspoons reduced-sodium soy sauce

1 teaspoon dark sesame oil

½ teaspoon honey

1 small tomato, diced

1 cup shredded Napa cabbage

½ cup shredded red cabbage

3 tablespoons chopped fresh cilantro

2 scallions, thinly sliced

Combine vinegar, ginger, soy sauce, sesame oil, and honey in large bowl. Add tomato, Napa cabbage, red cabbage, cilantro, and scallions; toss to mix well. Serve at once or cover and refrigerate up to 2 days.

CHANGE IT UP

Shrimp and Edamame Salad

Cook ¼ cup frozen shelled edamame in 1 cup water in small saucepan until tender, about 5 minutes. Drain and add to the salad with ¼ cup cooked baby shrimp.

Sesame Tofu Salad

Add ½ cup drained and cubed low-fat firm tofu, ½ cup baby spinach, and 1 teaspoon toasted sesame seeds to the salad.

Chinese Chicken Salad

Whisk 2 teaspoons reduced-fat peanut butter and 1 teaspoon hot water into the dressing. Add ¼ cup sliced cooked skinless and boneless chicken breast and ¼ cup chopped red bell pepper to the salad.

Shrimp and Edamame Salad

Crabmeat Salad with
Nectarine and Onion

Sweet and Savory California Salad

Serves 1 (about 3 cups)

2 tablespoons orange juice

2 teaspoons lime juice

$1/4$ teaspoon salt

$1/8$ teaspoon black pepper

$1/8$ teaspoon chili powder

2 cups baby arugula

$1/2$ navel orange, peeled and diced

$1/4$ avocado, peeled, pitted, and cut into 1-inch pieces

Whisk together orange juice, lime juice, salt, pepper, and chili powder in small bowl. Mound arugula leaves on plate. Top with orange and avocado and sprinkle with dressing.

CHANGE IT UP

Brown Rice Citrus Salad
Peel $1/2$ small red grapefruit and cut into sections. Add to the salad with $1/4$ cup cooked brown rice and 2 teaspoons dried cranberries.

....

Crabmeat Salad with Nectarine and Onion
Thinly slice $1/4$ small red onion. Add to the salad with $1/2$ cup cooked crabmeat and $1/2$ medium pitted and sliced nectarine.

....

Goat Cheese Salad with Almonds and Dates
Sprinkle the salad with 2 tablespoons soft crumbled goat cheese, 1 medium pitted and chopped date, and 1 teaspoon sliced toasted almonds.

Russian Beet and Carrot Salad

Serves 1 (about 1½ cups)

3 tablespoons plain fat-free Greek yogurt

2 teaspoons apple cider vinegar

1 cup sliced cooked beets

¼ cup shredded carrot

1 celery stalk, finely chopped

2 tablespoons minced red onion

¼ teaspoon salt

¼ teaspoon black pepper

Whisk yogurt and vinegar in large bowl. Add beets, carrot, celery, onion, salt, and pepper; toss to mix well.

CHANGE IT UP

 ### Beet Salad with Cucumber and Cottage Cheese
Add ½ cup diced cucumber and 1 tablespoon chopped fresh mint to the salad. Top with ¼ cup fat-free cottage cheese.

 ### Beet Salad with Egg and Dill
Slice 1 large hard-cooked egg and add to the salad with 2 tablespoons chopped fresh dill.

 ### Beet, Apple, and Walnut Salad
Add 1 small chopped Granny Smith apple and 1 tablespoon chopped toasted walnuts to the salad.

Beet Salad with Egg and Dill

Recipes by **PointsPlus** value

Index